MERRY DITTIES

Edited and arranged for
Piano, and Guitar by Norman Cazden

Illustrated by Abner Graboff

BONANZA BOOKS · NEW YORK

CONTENTS

INTRODUCTION

MERRY DITTIES is an unexpurgated collection of delectable songs and ballads from popular tradition. Most of them deal with the intimacies of men and women, the trials and the joys of love. Courting and disporting are described in delicate and imaginative fashion, with humor and sympathy. Traditional songs treat these affairs frankly, fairly, and with a notable maturity made memorable through delightful and haunting tunes. As the late folk singer, George Edwards, once remarked about *Captain Walker's Courtship*, which is a treatment of the widely known riddle song theme, "There no harm in it, there's no harm in it to anyone." We believe with him that the suggestive, uninhibited, often lusty passages in many of these songs, expressed through imagery that is at once bold and subtle, should offend no honest person.

These are songs of the people. Unlike the products of the commercial entertainment industry, songs formed from popular themes and images and handed on by word of mouth undergo rigorous selection and a communal and historical digestive process. Each singer must feel that a song is truthful, valuable, and beautiful, else it dies. Appearance in print at any particular time simply registers the form taken by a song strain in a certain time and locale. Oral improvisation continues to change and polish the song, while more deliberate literary efforts draw on motifs and expressions long in use. Thus elements in this group of songs recall some of the refreshing passages in Chaucer, Boccaccio, and Rabelais, not because they are derivative but because they have grown from the same store of popular legendry and idiom. Poets and composers have merely set down in specific lines and notes the ideas and the formulations, the tales, wordings, and sentiments which were current around them. Their success is measured by the extent to which they have faithfully reproduced and enlarged upon attitudes held in common with their fellows. Human and artistic truth has never been accessible to the squeamish.

There are those who may say that while the story and incident of one or another of these songs may be decorous enough, and while the restraint and wit in references to sex in traditional lore are well appreciated, it remains problematical whether we ought to issue for general use a tale like *The Little Scotch Girl*, for instance, in which a

1

a girl gets into bed with a man. To this we reply, borrowing the direct if irreverent manner of such ballads, that for every girl who gets into bed with a man there has to be a first time. It seems a fairly widespread practice and we are not disposed to discourage it! Most of us will incline to join in the toast to the little Scotch girl's bonny, bonny blue, and to hear the little birds sing all on a summer's morning.

Indeed, perhaps the proper and constructive answer to the manufacture of the truly uncouth and salacious articles so widespread today is the bringing together of the hearty, sensitive, and profoundly moral merry ditties of tradition, which have something to say and are suffused with the open, sympathetic lyricism of people who sing for and of themselves.

All of the tunes and texts in this book are basically folk song materials re-cast for songbook use. They have been compiled from songbooks and broadsides dating back to the seventeenth-century, and from many sources in oral tradition. Most of them are rare, and their forms here unique. In the notes which follow something of the origin of each song has been given. And, with utmost care for their original qualities, certain changes and additions have been made. Songs heard in closely related variants have been combined into a single form. Many tunes have been transposed to a range more suitable for general singing. Slight deviations in the tunes for different stanzas have been omitted. Many texts have been completed from broadsides or other printed sources so as to have all of the ballad stories and their fine popular imagery. Simple guitar-chord signs have been added as guides for accompaniment on the guitar or other plucked instrument and also on the piano, together with instructions for their use, and full piano accompaniments are also provided.

Our object has been a practical songbook stressing musical and human values. Where some of these songs are known in other, perhaps widely different versions, we hope that charity, curiosity, and free impulse will allow our forms to be learned, sung, and played with relish.

Rolling In The Dew

A conversation piece between the shy
country maid and the sophisticated gallant.

2 "Oh, may I go with you, my pretty fair maid,
  With your rosy cheeks and your coal-black hair?"
  "Why, just as you please," she answered me,
  "Oh, it's rolling in the dew makes the milkmaid
    fair."

3 "Suppose I should kiss you, my pretty fair maid,
  With your rosy cheeks and your coal-black hair?"
  "The wind would blow it off," she answered me,
  "Oh, it's rolling in the dew makes the milkmaid
    fair."

4 "Suppose I should marry you, my pretty fair maid,
  With your rosy cheeks and your coal-black hair?"
  "Why, do as you please," she answered me,
  "Oh, it's rolling in the dew makes the milkmaid
    fair."

5 "And would you be constant, my pretty fair maid,
  With your rosy cheeks and your coal-black hair?"
  "Oh, that I cannot promise," she answered me,
  "For it's rolling in the dew makes the milkmaid
    fair."

3

I Know My Love

New Words and Music by Norman Cazden

It is a pity that this wry plaint about careless love has sometimes
been miscast to suggest that the girl was fickle.

1. I know my love by his way of walk-ing, And I know my love by his way of talk-ing, And I know my love by his suit of blue, Yet if my love leaves me, what will I do? For though he cries he loves

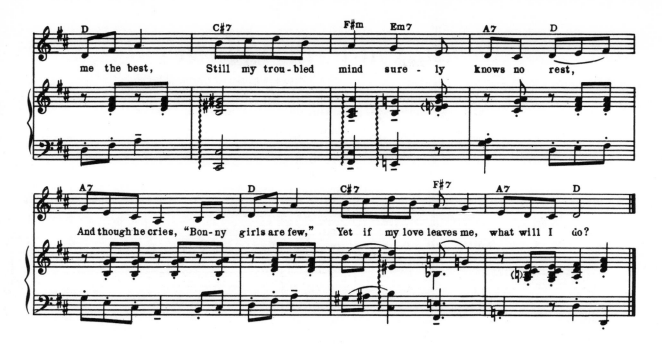

me the best, Still my trou-bled mind sure-ly knows no rest,

And though he cries, "Bon-ny girls are few," Yet if my love leaves me, what will I do?

2 My true love sighed when he courted me
And stole from me my liberty,
So he won my heart and my free good will,
And surely he knows I do love him still.
(refrain)

3 Love is so careless of grief and woe
When he followed me through frost and snow;
But sad the change that time does bring,
Now my love goes by, and he says nothing.
(refrain)

4 There is an ale house in our town
Where my love goes to set him down,
Then he takes another on his knee;
O, can you think how that vexes me! *(refrain)*

5 It vexes me, and I'll tell you why,
It's because she has more gold than I;
But her gold will waste and her beauty pass,
Soon he'll turn again to some other lass.
(refrain)

6 If my love knew, I would wash and wring,
If my love knew, I would weave and spin,
I'd have a coat of the finest weft,
But the want of money leaves me bereft.
(refrain)

7 I wish, I wish, but it's all in vain,
I wish that I were a maid again,
For free again I shall never be
Till red apples grow on a cherry tree. *(refrain)*

5

What Can the Matter Be?

New Words and Music by Norman Cazden

The beginning of this song, and the nice tune, are widely
known, but don't miss this chance to discover a fuller
insight into the character of the impatient girl.

1. Oh, dear, what can the mat-ter be? Dear, dear, what can the mat-ter be,
Oh, dear, what can the mat-ter be, John-ny's so long at the fair.

He prom-ised to buy me a fair-ing, 'twould please me, And
then for a kiss, oh, he vowed he would tease me, He prom-ised to buy me a

6

bunch of blue rib-bons To tie up my bon-ny brown hair.

2. Oh, dear, what can the mat-ter be? Dear, dear, what can the mat-ter be,

Oh, dear, what can the mat-ter be? John-ny's so long at the fair.

2 Oh, dear, what can the matter be?
Dear, dear, what can the matter be?
Oh, dear, what can the matter be,
Johnny's so long at the fair.
He promised to buy me a pair of sleeve buttons,
A pair of new garters to cost him but tuppence,
A pair of red stockings to go with the ribbons
That tie up my bonny brown hair.

3 Oh, dear, what can the matter be?
Dear, dear, what can the matter be?
Oh, dear, what can the matter be,
Johnny's so long at the fair.
He promised to buy me a basket of posies,
A garland of lilies, a gift of red roses,
A little straw hat to set off the blue ribbons
To tie up my bonny brown hair.

4 Oh, dear, what can the matter be?
Dear, dear, what can the matter be?
Oh, dear, what can the matter be,
Johnny's so long at the fair.
He promised to buy me a ring and a locket,
A few little things just to keep in my pocket,
Some shiny new pins for the bunch of blue ribbons
To tie up my bonny brown hair.

5 Oh, dear, see how he's running,
Dear, dear, see, he is coming,
Oh, dear, see how he's running,
Johnny's come back from the fair.
He has brought me a delicate basket of posies,
A garland of lilies, a gift of red roses,
He's given me a kiss with the bunch of blue
    ribbons
That tie up my bonny brown hair.

7

The Maid on the Shore

New Words and Music by Norman Cazden

A legendary song about a siren who is very much of this world.
Her charms are equal to those of the unusual melody.

1. There was a fair maiden I dearly adored; Her beauty, it did shine clear, O, And all she could find for to ease her sad mind was to roam all alone on the shore, O shore, Was to roam all alone on the shore.

2 And there was a sea captain who plowed the
    salt sea,
Who sailed the seas all over,
This beautiful maiden he chanced for to spy,
"Don't I wish that I had her on board, O board,
Don't I wish that I had her on board!"

3 Then the captain said unto his small cabin boy,
"If you bring me that maid on the shore, O,
I will make you a present, I can't tell you what,
It'll be something costli and dear, O dear,
It'll be something costli and dear."

8

4 The steward, he ran and he lowered the boat,
And quickly he rowed it to shore, O,
And these were the very first words that he said,
"Kind madam, won't you come on board, O,
board,
Kind madam, won't you come on board?

5 "Our captain has jewels, our captain has rings,
Just such things as you ladies do wear, O,
And if you will come and buy some of him,
We will row you along by the shore, O shore,
We will row you along by the shore."

6 It's "I haven't no money to buy them of him,
And such things are costli and dear, O!"
"But our captain is kind, he will trust you to them
Till sometime he'll repair to the shore, O shore,
Till sometime he'll repair to the shore."

7 So by coaxing, persuading, she entered the boat,
And quickly he rowed her on board, O,
And our captain, being pleased, he bade them
come on,
Saying, "Fare ye well, sorrows and care, O care,"
Saying, "Fare ye well, sorrows and care.

8 "Now I will treat to the richeri wine
That sparkles so bright and so clear, O,
And then you may sing us a merrili song
To compare with our merrili crew, O crew,
To compare with our merrili crew."

9 So she seated herself in the stern of the boat,
Her voice was so fair and so clear, O
And she sang them so sweet, so neat and
complete,
Sang the captain and sailors to sleep, O sleep,
Sang the captain and sailors to sleep.

10 She robbed them of silver, she robbed them of
gold,
She robbed them of costli a-ware, O,
And the captain's bright sword she used for an
oar
For to row herself back to the shore, O shore,
For to row herself back to the shore.

11 "O, were my men crazy or were they all drunk,
Or were they sunk deep in despair, O,
To see her get away, with her beauty so gay?
Don't I wish that I had her once more, O more,
Don't I wish that I had her once more!"

12 And yonder she stands all alone on the strand
A-waving her handkerchief fair, O,
Saying, "You are the captain that plowed these
salt seas,
And I'm still a maid on the shore, O shore,
O, I am the maid on the shore."

The Little Scotch Girl

New Words and Music by Norman Cazden

This is the only complete version located in the United States, with a unique tune. The old Scottish ballad is in line with the tradition from which Chaucer learned many a lesson.

1. There was a lit-tle Scotch girl, she went down-town Some white-fish for to buy, There she got ac-quaint-ed with a lit-tle town clerk, And he

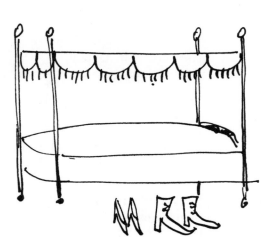

2 "Where are you going, sweet maid?" said he,
   "And whereon do you be?
   For let this night be ever so dark,
   I'll come and I'll visit thee, O thee,
   I'll come and I'll visit thee."

3 "My mamma locks the door within,
   My papa keeps the key,
   Unless you be a silly old witch
   You'll never come in to me, O me,
   You'll never come in to me.

4 "Unless you have a ladder built
   Of thirty steps and three
   And build it up to the chimney top
   And then come down to me, O me,
   And then come down to me."

10

TRO - © Copyright 1958 - ANDOVER MUSIC, INC., New York City, N.Y.
Used by Permission

fol-lowed her speed-i - li, O li, And he fol-lowed her speed-i - li.

5 The little town clerk, he had a brother,
  And a wee little wit was he,
  And he has built a great muckle ladder
  Of thirty steps and three, O three,
  Of thirty steps and three.

6 He put the cleat to his right shoulder
  And a creel butt to the pin,
  And he drew them up to the chimney top
  And he let the bonny clerk in, O in,
  And he let the bonny clerk in.

7 The old folks layed in the room close by
  And, hearing what was said,
  "I'll lay my life," said the silly old wife,
  "There's a man in our daughter's bed, O bed,
  There's a man in our daughter's bed."

8 The good old man, he went upstairs
  To see, could this be true?
  When she drew the bonny clerk close in her arms
  And covered him over with blue, O blue,
  And she covered him over with blue.

9 "What brings you here, papa," she said,
  "What brings you here so late?
  You disturb me of my evening prayers,
  And O, but they are sweet, O sweet,
  And O, but they are sweet!"

10 "Pray on, pray on, my daughter dear,
  And see you do it right.
  If ever a woman lost her sense,
  Your mother did this night, O night,
  Your mother did this night!"

11 The good old man, he went downstairs,
  Said, "You did not tell me true,
  Our daughter has a great muckle book in her
    arms,
  She's a-praying for me and you, O you,
  She's a-praying for me and you!"

12 The good old man, he went to bed
  Lest something more be said,
  But woe be to the silly old wife,
  For she was waking yet, O yet,
  For she was waking yet.

13 They had not kissed, nor very long hugged,
  As lovers do when they meet,
  "You may say as you like, you silly old man,
  But I hear somebody speak, O speak,
  I hear somebody speak."

14 "Get up yourself, you silly old wife,
  And go yourself to see,
  For between you and your dear daughter
  I haven't once closed an eye, O eye,
  I haven't once closed an eye."

15 The silly old woman, she went upstairs
  To see, could this be true?
  And what in the devil should take her foot,
  But into the creel she flew, O flew,
  But into the creel she flew!

16 The brother at the chimney top,
  Now finding the creel was full,
  He put the cleat to his right shoulder
  And fast to her did pull, O pull,
  And fast to her did pull.

17 He shook her up, he shook her down,
  He gave her a right downfall
  Till every rib in the old girl's back
  Played knick-knack on the wall, O wall,
  Played knick-knack on the wall!

18 Here's to the blue, the bonny, bonny blue,
  And we wish the blue does well,
  While every woman that is jealous of her
    daughter
  Might fall into the creel, O creel,
  Might fall into the creel!

11

The Trooper and the Tailor

New Words and Music by Norman Cazden

Like *The Jolly Boatswain* and its relatives, a song about an unfortunate tailor
lad, little known in its lines and with a neat and unusual tune.

1. There was a good black-smith in Lon-don did dwell, He had a fair la-dy, he loved her right well, He had a fair la-dy, he loved her right well, And this

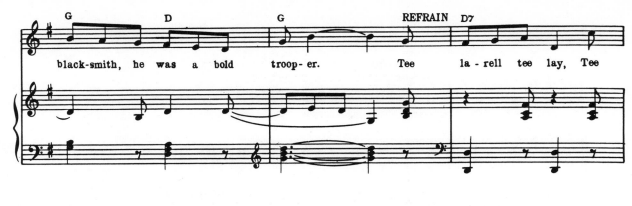

black-smith, he was a bold troop-er. Tee la - rell tee lay, Tee

la - rell, tee lay, Tee la - rell, tee la - rell, tee lie - do.

2 There was a young tailor who lived close by,
  And on this fair lady did he cast an eye.
  He swore he would have her, or else he would die,
  For he did not admire the trooper. *(refrain)*

3 The tailor came over awhile after night
  To press for the favor of his heart's delight,
  Saying, "Three guineas I'll give for lodging
    tonight,
  For I hear that your husband's on duty."
                    (refrain)

4 "Oh yes, little tailor, you've guessed very right,
  My husband's on duty for this very night,
  But if he should come, it would set me affright,
  For you know that my husband's a trooper."
                    (refrain)

The Trooper and the Tailor   **VERSION 2**

8. So she tripped it and trapped it all down the old stair, With

kiss-es and com-pli-ments she met him there. "But for kiss-es and com-pli-ments

5 They blowed out the light and to bed they did
   run,
   They hadn't been there long before fun had
   begun.
   They huddled and cuddled, and both fell asleep,
   And they had no more thought of the trooper.
   (refrain)

6 The trooper came home in the midst of the night,
   He rapped on the door, which gave them a
   great fright.
   "O hide me, O hide me, my sweet heart's delight,
   For I hear the bold raps of the trooper!"
   (refrain)

7 "There's a three-cornered cupboard behind the
   old door,
   I'll put you in that, you'll be safe and secure,
   While I must go down, and I'll open the door
   To let in my husband, the trooper."   *(refrain)*

8 So she tripped it and trapped it all down the
   old stair,
   With kisses and compliments she met him there.
   "But for kisses and compliments I do not care,
   Go light me a fire," said the trooper.   *(refrain)*

9 "The fire is all out, and there's no fire stuff,
   So come to bed, darling, you'll be warm enough!"
   "There's that three-cornered cupboard behind the
   old door,
   And I'll burn it this night," said the trooper.
   (refrain)

10 "O husband, dear husband, its grandma's
    desire,
    And the three-cornered cupboard's too good for
    the fire,
    And in it's my game-cock, which I do admire."
    "I'll see your game-cock," said the trooper.
    (refrain)

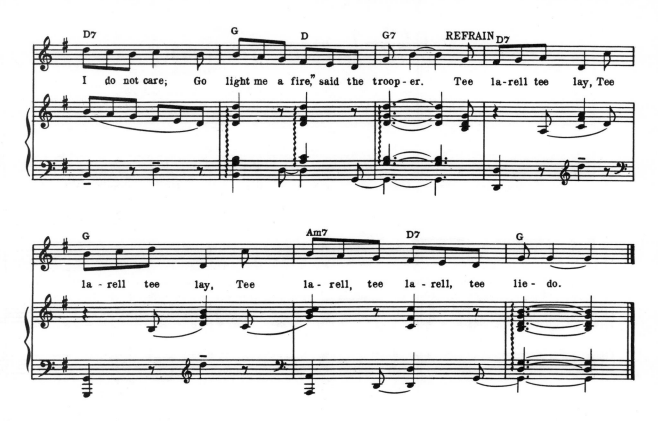

I do not care; Go light me a fire," said the troop-er. Tee la-rell tee lay, Tee

la-rell tee lay, Tee la-rell, tee la-rell, tee lie-do.

11 So he went to the cupboard and opened the door,
There sot the little tailor, so safe and secure.
Grabbed the nape of his neck, yanked him out
on the floor,
"I'll fight your game-cock," said the trooper.
(refrain)

12 He kicked and he cuffed him and used him
severe,
With his own pair of shears he cut off his two
ears.
"And for this night's lodging you've paid very
dear!"
And away went the poor croppèd tailor.
(refrain)

The Little Sparrow

New Words and Music by Norman Cazden
A complaining song with a melody in the best ballad style.

1. Come all you fair and tender ladies, Take warning how you court young men, They are like the star of a summer's morning, They will first appear and then they're gone.

2 They'll tell to you some pleasing story,
They'll declare to you their love is true,
Straightway they'll go and court another,
And that's the love they have for you.

3 When I did meet my own true lover,
I thought he surely was my own,
But now he's gone and found another
And left me here alone to mourn.

4 He said his heart did burn like fire
Whenever my face he did see,
But it was all for my deception,
He never meant for to marry me.

5 If I had known before I courted
That true love was so hard to win,
I'd have locked my heart with a key of golden
And held it down with a silver pin.

6 It was last night you were sweetly sleeping
And in my arms found your repose,
While I, poor girl, was broken-hearted
A-listening to the wild winds blow.

7 Just go and leave me if you have to,
For it can never trouble me,
It's in your heart to love another,
And in my grave I'd rather be.

16

The Little Sparrow   VERSION 2

9. I wish I was a lit-tle spar-row And I had wings to fly a-way, I'd fly till I came to my false lov-er, And while he talked, I would be by.

8 I know the day is surely coming
When love will make an end of me,
For deep inside the torment's burning,
Crying for my love deserting me.

9 I wish I was a little sparrow
And I had wings to fly away,
I'd fly till I came to my false lover,
And while he talked, I would be by.

10 Young man, never cast your eyes on beauty,
For beauty's a thing that will decay,
The prettiest flowers grow in the garden,
They soon will wither and fade away.

11 Oh, love is handsome, love is charming,
And love is warming when it's new,
But love grows cold when it's left to smolder
And it fades away with the morning dew.

Let's Have Another Round

New Words and Music by Norman Cazden

Good fellowship and sage morality from a lumber camp setting.

1. I'm a cel-e-brat-ed lum-ber-man, my du-ty I nev-er shirk, I have cut more wood than an-y man from Saug-er-ties to New York, It's a large in-ter-ro-ga-tion, boys, how I get through my work While I'm sit-ting here con-sum-ing beer, Let's have an-oth-er round.

18

2 Now, the man who drinks his fill of beer and
    goes to bed quite mellow,
  He lives as he ought to live, and dies a hearty
    fellow,
  Let's have another round, my boys, and let the
    glass run over,
  For tonight we'll merry, merry be, tomorrow
    we'll get sober.

3 The girl who gets a little kiss and runs to tell
    her mother
  Will be slow to find what she's looking for, she
    seldom gets another,
  But the girl who gets a little kiss and asks for
    another
  Will get what she is asking for, let's have another
    round.

4 The man that courts a pretty girl and uses her
    for pleasure
  Is a knave until he marries her and gives her
    of good measure,
  The man who drinks what he likes best and has
    his friends over
  Will live until he dies, and then he'll have another
    round.

19

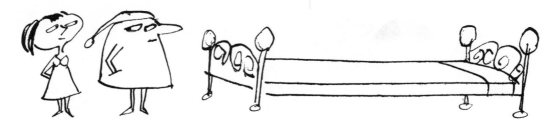

Captain Walker's Courtship

New Words and Music by Norman Cazden

A fuller form of the well-known *Riddle Song* about the cherry
without a stone and the chicken without a bone. The girl
from Maiden Lane seems well prepared to lose the contest
of wit. The tune is Irish; so there is of course
a version in Yiddish from Byelorussia.

1. It's of a rich man's daugh-ter who lived in Maid-en Lane, She
met with Cap-tain Walk-er, a keep-er of the game. He
says, "My pret-ty fair maid, if it was-n't for the law, Then

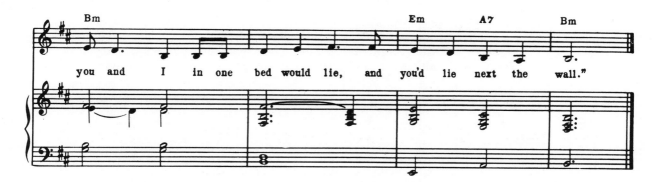

you and I in one bed would lie, and you'd lie next the wall."

2 "O, hold your tongue, young man," says she,
   "and do not bother me,
   'Fore you and I in one bed shall lie, these
      questions answer me,
   These questions you shall answer me, as I to
      you do call,
   Then you and I in one bed shall lie, but I
      won't lie next the wall."

3 "What is rounder than my finger ring, what's
      higher than the trees,
   And what is worse than womankind, what is
      deeper than the sea,
   What bird sings best, what tree first buds, where
      does the dew first fall?
   Then you and I in one bed shall lie, but I
      won't lie next the wall."

4 "The globe is rounder than your ring, Heaven's
      higher than the trees,
   And men are worse than womankind, Hell is
      deeper than the sea,
   The thrush sings best, and the yew first buds,
      in the air the dew first falls,
   Now you and I in one bed shall lie, and you'll
      lie next the wall."

5 "O, hold your tongue, young man," says she,
   "and do not me perplex,
   Before you and I in one bed shall lie, three
      dishes you must dress,
   Three dishes you must dress for me, as I to
      you do call,
   Then you and I in one bed shall lie, but I
      won't lie next the wall.

6 "All for my breakfast you must dress a chicken
      without a bone;
   And for my dinner you must dress a cherry
      without a stone;
   All for my supper you must dress a bird without
      a gall,
   Then you and I in one bed shall lie, but I won't
      lie next the wall."

7 "Now, when the chicken is in the egg, I'm sure
      it has no bone;
   When the cherry is in the blossom, I'm sure it
      has no stone;
   And there's the dove, that gentle bird, it flies
      without a gall,
   Now you and I in one bed shall lie, and you'll
      lie next the wall."

8 It's time to call up the story and for to end
      this song:
   This couple soon got married and happy were
      for long.
   This maid being generous-hearted, his heart she
      did enthrall,
   He took the fair maid in his arms and rolled her
      from the wall.

I Wonder When
I Shall Be Married

New Words and Music by Norman Cazden

The old maid of any age who has lost hope remains a pathetic figure in every age. Another version of this song was adapted by Robert Burns.

1. I won-der I nev-er got mar-ried, Um, ah! nev-er got mar-ried, Such a beau-ti-ful crea-ture as I. I mean to lay hold on some-bod-y, Um, ah! hold on some-bod-y, Be-fore I am tak-en a-way. And I won-der when I shall be mar-ried, Um,

ah! when I shall be mar-ried, For my beau-ty's be-gin-ning to fade.

2 I fear that too long I have tarried,
 Um, ah! too long I have tarried,
 I fear I shall be an old maid.
 My mother is anxious and worried,
 Um, ah! anxious and worried,
 She has two other daughters besides.
 And I wonder when I shall be married,
 Um, ah! when I shall be married,
 For my beauty's beginning to fade.

3 My father has forty good shillings,
 Um, ah! forty good shillings,
 He's put them away all for me.
 My mother says she is right willing,
 Um, ah! she is right willing,
 That I shall have all when they die.
 And I wonder when I shall be married,
 Um, ah! when I shall be married,
 For my beauty's beginning to fade.

4 My mother has saved an old dipper,
 Um, ah! has saved an old dipper,
 All for to remind her of me.
 And she says if I marry to suit her,
 Um, ah! if I marry to suit her,
 I sure shall have that when she dies.
 And I wonder when I shall be married,
 Um, ah! when I shall be married,
 For my beauty's beginning to fade.

5 My shoes have been sent out for mending,
 Um, ah! sent out for mending,
 My buckles are both in the chest.
 My stockings are ready for sending,
 Um, ah! ready for sending,
 Then I'll be as brave as the rest.
 And I wonder when I shall be married,
 Um, ah! when I shall be married,
 For my beauty's beginning to fade.

6 I've a knife and a fork and a trencher,
 Um, ah! a fork and a trencher,
 And ah! won't I be a fine bride.
 Don't you think it will be a great bargain,
 Um, ah! 'twill be a great bargain,
 When someone gets married to me?
 And I wonder when I shall be married,
 Um, ah! when I shall be married,
 For my beauty's beginning to fade.

7 My father will buy me a ladle,
 Um, ah! will buy me a ladle,
 At my wedding we'll have a good song.
 My uncle will give me a cradle,
 Um, ah! will give me a cradle,
 To rock my child in when it's young.
 And I wonder when I shall be married,
 Um, ah! when I shall be married,
 For my beauty's beginning to fade.

8 Now who would not like a gay lady,
 Um, ah! would like a gay lady,
 Whose petticoat soon will be dyed.
 With a dipper, a cradle and shilling,
 Um, ah! a cradle and shilling,
 That they'll surely get when I die?
 But I wonder when I shall be married,
 Um, ah! when I shall be married,
 For my beauty's beginning to fade.

23

A-roving

New Words and Music by Norman Cazden

A sailor's song much in favor among landlubbers.
The closely matched tune keeps listeners agog.

1. In Am-ster-dam there lives a maid, Mark well what I do say, In Am-ster-dam there lives a maid, And she is mis-tress of her trade. I'll go no more a-rov-ing with you fair maid.

REFRAIN

A - rov - ing, a - rov - ing, since rov - ing's been my ru - eye - in, I'll
go no more a - rov - ing with you, fair maid.

2 The last six months I'd been to sea,
  Mark well what I do say,
  The last six months I'd been to sea,
  And boys, this maid looked good to me.
    I'll go no more a-roving with you, fair maid.
      (refrain)

3 She was a girl so passing fair,
  Mark well what I do say,
  She was a girl so passing fair,
  She had blue eyes and curly hair . . .
      (refrain)

4 I took this maid out for a walk,
  Mark well what I do say,
  I took this maid out for a walk,
  And we had such a lovely talk . . .

      (refrain)

5 With love for her my heart did burn,
  Mark well what I do say,
  With love for her my heart did burn,
  I thought she loved me in return . . .
      (refrain)

6 I put my arm around her waist,
  Mark well·what I do say,
  I put my arm around her waist,
  She said, "Young man, you're in some haste . . ."
      (refrain)

7 I helped that maid off with her shoe,
Mark well what I do say,
I helped that maid off with her shoe,
She said, "Young man, you're rather low..."
(*refrain*)

8 I laid my hand upon her knee,
Mark well what I do say,
I laid my hand upon her knee,
She said, "Young man, you're rather free..."
(*refrain*)

9 I laid my head upon her bust,
Mark well what I do say,
I laid my head upon her bust,
She said, "Young man, now, if you must..."
(*refrain*)

10 I took her by her shoulders wide,
Mark well what I do say,
I took her by her shoulders wide,
She looked at me and gently cried...
(*refrain*)

11 At last we chatted and chaffed away,
Mark well what I do say,
At last we chatted and chaffed away,
"Please, don't you leave me here today..."
(*refrain*)

12 She swore that she'd be true to me,
Mark well what I do say,
She swore that she'd be true to me,
And she spent my money fast and free...
(*refrain*)

13 But when my money was gone and spent,
Mark well what I do say,
But when my money was gone and spent,
Then off to another man she went...
(*refrain*)

14 By this it's well that I have learned,
Mark well what I do say,
By this it's well that I have learned,
To keep the money I have earned...
(*refrain*)

Billy Boy

New Words and Music by Norman Cazden

Billy's young thing has some surprising qualities, but
she knows just what to do in the clinches.

1. Oh where have you been, Bil - ly boy, Bil - ly boy, Oh where have you been, charm - ing Bil - ly? I have been to seek a wife, she's the joy of my life, She's a young thing, and can - not leave her moth - er.

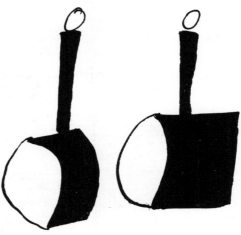

2 Oh, where does she live, Billy boy, Billy boy,
   Oh, where does she live, charming Billy?
She lives just over the hill,
Forty miles beyond the mill,
   *She's a young thing, and cannot leave her
      mother.*

3 Did she bid you to come in, Billy boy, Billy
      boy . . .
Yes, she bid me to come in,
There's a dimple on her chin . . .

4 Did she ask to take your hat, Billy boy, Billy
      boy . . .
Yes, she asked to take my hat
And she fed it to the cat . . .

5 Did she set for you a chair, Billy boy, Billy
      boy . . .
Yes, she set for me a chair,
But the bottom wasn't there . . .

6 Did she have you stay to supper, Billy boy,
      Billy boy . . .
Yes, she had me stay to supper,
The very best of bread and butter . . .

29

7 Did she tell you her age, Billy boy, Billy boy...
   She's three times six, four times seven,
   Twenty-eight and near eleven...

8 Do you think she is full-grown, Billy boy, Billy
      boy...
   She's as tall as any pine
   And as straight as a pumpkin vine...

9 Can she make a cherry pie, Billy boy, Billy
    boy...
She can make a cherry pie
Quick as a cat can wink it's eye...

10 Can she milk a brindle cow, Billy boy, Billy
    boy ...
She can milk 'most any cow,
When her mother shows her how...

11 Can she bake a loaf of bread, Billy boy, Billy
    boy...
She can bake a loaf of bread,
Use it for an oven lid...

12 Can she milk a heifer calf, Billy boy, Billy
    boy ...
She can milk a heifer calf
And miss the bucket more than half...

13 Can she row a boat to shore, Billy boy, Billy
    boy...
She can row a boat to shore
Without a paddle or an oar...

14 Can she patch a pair of britches, Billy boy,
    Billy boy ...
She can patch a pair of britches
With the cutest little stitches...

15 Did she snuggle close to you, Billy boy, Billy
    boy...
Yes, she snuggled close to me
As the bark upon a tree...

16 Did she kiss you goodnight, Billy boy, Billy
    boy ...
Yes, she kissed me goodnight
And she hugged me very tight...

17 Did she light you up to bed, Billy boy, Billy
    boy ...
Yes, she lit me up to bed,
But she shook her dainty head...

VERSION 3

17. Did she light you up to bed, Bil - ly boy, Bil - ly boy, Did she

light you up to bed, charm-ing Bil- ly? Yes, she lit me up to bed, but she

shook her dain - ty head, She's a young thing, and can - not leave her moth - er.

Katey Morey

The sly and crafty rogue finds himself up a tree
with a rollicking refrain for company.

New Words and Music by Norman Cazden

1. Come, all you sly and craft-y rogues, Come lis-ten to my sto-ry. I'll tell you how I worked a plan To cheat one, Kat-ey Mor-ey

REFRAIN

With my whack! fol lath-er-o, tath-er-o, leath-er-o, Whack! fol lath-er-o, tath-er-o lay.

2 I went down to her father's house,
Just like a clever fellow,
I told her that the plums were ripe,
Had just begun to mellow.

(refrain)

3 I told her that my sister Sue
Was down in yonder bower,
She wanted her to come down there
And spend one half an hour.

(refrain)

32

4 I did not have to ask her twice,
　She put on her best bonnet.
　My heart was beating very fast
　As across the field she ran it.

　　　　　　　　　　　　　　　(refrain)

5 I waited there till she had gone,
　Then quickly I pursued her,
　I caught her near the plum-tree there
　With purpose to delude her.

　　　　　　　　　　　　　　　(refrain)

6 I told her that my sister Sue
　Knew nothing of the matter,
　"You must comply, or you must die
　I have no time to flatter."

　　　　　　　　　　　　　　　(refrain)

7 She seemed to be pleased, my hand she squeezed,
　"But there's one thing I fear, sir,
　My father's coming by this way
　And he will catch us here, sir.

　　　　　　　　　　　　　　　(refrain)

8 "But if you will strive to climb this tree
　While father's going his way, sir,
　Then we'll go down in yonder brake
　And there we'll sport and play, sir."

　　　　　　　　　　　　　　　(refrain)

9 So then I strove to climb above,
　Not being the least offended,
　While Katey Morey stood at the roots
　To see how I ascended.

　　　　　　　　　　　　　　　(refrain)

10 I twitched and jerked and made such work,
　　It stuck right into my crop, sir,
　　I caught and swore, my britches tore
　　Until I reached the top, sir.

　　　　　　　　　　　　　　　(refrain)

11 Kate says to me, "You're up the tree,
　　And you look much like an owl, sir,
　　You can eat your plums and crack the stones.
　　And have your fun alone, sir."

　　　　　　　　　　　　　　　(refrain)

12 Then Katey heeled it over the field
　　And left me there distracted.
　　I puffed and swore at Katey More'
　　To see how she had acted.

　　　　　　　　　　　　　　　(refrain)

10. I twitched and jerked and made such work, It stuck right in-to my crop, sir. I caught and swore, my britch-es tore Un-til I reached the top, sir, With my whack! fol lath-er-o, tath-er-o, leath-er-o, Whack! fol lath-er-o, tath-er-o lay.

13 I straightway did descend the tree
    With many a stretch and bound, sir,
    But Katey Morey was out of sight
    Before I reached the ground, sir.

(refrain)

14 Next morning when I'd thought it out,
    I wasn't the least offended,
    I went to Kate and married her,
    And now my britches get mended.

(refrain)

15 It's well I've clumb the tallest tree
    That ever bore a plum, sir,
    We'll try a slip for grafting it
    And see what fruit it'll be, sir.

(refrain)

16 My plan is crossed up, I've sung enough,
    It's time to quit my rhyming,
    Now every time Kate smiles at me,
    She makes me think of climbing.

(refrain)

My Pretty Little Maid

New Words and Music by Norman Cazden

One of a group of conversation pieces in which the country lass outwits the smart feller from the city. The nice refrain shows what she keeps in reserve.

1.Oh, where are you go-ing, my pret-ty lit-tle maid? I'm go-ing a-milk-ing, kind sir, she said, Sing ree, sing low, sing fare you well; Sing ree, sing low, and fare you well, my dear.

2 May I go along, my pretty little maid?
Do just as you please, kind sir, she said. *(refrain)*

3 Who is your father, my pretty little maid?
My father is a farmer, kind sir, she said.
(refrain)

4 And who is your mother, my pretty little maid?
A wife to my father, kind sir, she said. *(refrain)*

5 What is your fortune, my pretty little maid?
A cow and a little calf, kind sir, she said.
(refrain)

6 Then I won't marry you, my pretty little maid?
And nobody asked you, kind sir, she said.
(refrain)

7 Why, then I must leave you, my pretty little maid.
The sooner, the better, kind sir, she said. *(refrain)*

35

Jennifer Gently

New Words and Music by Norman Cazden

This belongs to the family of songs that includes *Dando* and *The Wee Cooper o' Fife*. The wife is "gentle" in the sense of having been gentled in her upbringing, but she ends up properly chastened.

2 She would not into the kitchen go,
   Come, Jennifer gently, my Rosamarie,
For fear of spoiling her comely hue,
   As the dew flies over the green valley.

3 She would not card, nor would she spin...
For fear of spoiling her delicate skin...

4 She would not wash, nor would she wring...
For fear of spoiling her golden ring...

5 She would not bake, nor would she brew...
For fear of spoiling her new white shoes...

36

12. "I'll tell my fa-ther and all my kin, Come, Jen-ni-fer gen-tly, my Ro-sa-ma-rie, That you've hit me with a hick-or-y limb, As the dew flies o-ver the green val-ley."

6 The first day I came home from plow . . .
   "O wife, is my dinner ready now?" . . .

7 "There lies a crust of bread on the shelf . . .
   If you want any more, go help yourself . . ."

8 I took up my knife, went out by the barn . . .
   And I cut two hickories, long as my arm . . .

9 I went straightway to my sheepfold . . .
   And downed an old sheep with a big, long
      pole . . .

10 I hung him up on two strong pins . . .
   And out of his skin I soon jerked him . . .

11 I put the sheepskin on my wife's back . . .
   And I made those two hickories
      whickety-whack . . .

12 "I'll tell my father and all my kin . . .
   That you've hit me with a hickory limb . . .

13 "You can tell your father and all your kin . . .
   I'm only tanning an old sheepskin . . ."

14 "I'll tell my mother and sisters three .
   Just how you have lambasted me . . ."

15 "You can tell your mother and all of your
      friends . . .
   I've whipped you once, and I'll do it again . . ."

16 The next time I came home from plow . . .
   "It's good to see you, and how do you do?" . . .

17 She flew to the kitchen, the table was spread . . .
   And kindly she set down with nary a word . . .

37

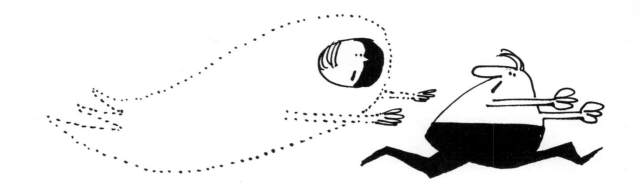

Unfortunate Miss Bailey

A very popular hit song of about 1800, the tune has been
used for numerous parodies, including *The Hunters of Kentucky.*
No one has ever been observed taking this as a sad tale.

1. A cap-tain bold of Hal - i - fax who
lived in coun - try quar - ters Se - duced a maid, who hanged her - self one

38

Monday in her garters. His guilty conscience smited him, he lost his stomach daily, He took to drinking ratafee and thought upon Miss Bailey.

REFRAIN

Bai - ley. Oh, Miss Bai - ley, un - for - tun - ate Miss Bai - ley.

2 One night, as he lay on his bed, 'cause he had got a fever,
Said he, "I am a handsome man, but I'm a gay deceiver."
At twelve o'clock that very night his candle burned quite palely,
A ghost stepped up to his bedside and cried, "Behold, Miss Bailey!"
Oh, Miss Bailey, unfortunate Miss Bailey.

3 "Avaunt, Miss Bailey," then he cried, "Your face looks white and mealy."
"Oh, Captain Smith," the ghost replied, "You've used me ungenteely,
The Coroner's quest goes hard with me, because I've acted fraily,
And Parson Briggs won't bury me, though I'm a dead Miss Bailey."
Oh, Miss Bailey, unfortunate Miss Bailey.

4 "Dear ghost," said he, "since you and I accounts must once for all close,
There is a one-pound note in my regimental small-clothes,
'Twill bribe the sexton for your grave." The ghost then vanished gaily,
Saying, "Bless you, wicked Captain Smith! Remember poor Miss Bailey!"
Oh, Miss Bailey, unfortunate Miss Bailey.

The Poor Countryman

New Words and Music by Norman Cazden
Somewhat related to *My Ducksie Has Fled,* but actually
a song of unknown origin on the same general theme.
The tune makes an excellent squirrel-cage jig.

1.I'm a poor coun-try-man from the town of Ath-lone, I'm

sad to my heart that I ev-er left home; I went down to Bel-fast, my

2 When I got to Belfast, I shortly did meet
With a fair one who asked me down to Peter
Street
To dance with her, "But I can't dance very well,
And I'm bound to seek out where my cousin
does dwell." *(refrain)*

3 She says, "Cousin mine, you are going astray,
And if you just follow, I'll show you the way!
By ten o'clock I will put you on the train,
You can give me a call when you're in town
again. *(refrain)*

4 "Now, if you can't dance, surely you'll have a
treat,
A glass of hot brandy and something to eat."
So we walked down through Williston, she
carried my coat,
And we booked us a pleasure-trip on the
steamboat. *(refrain)*

5 She hired us a cab for to not wet her feet,
Took me and my baggage to New Market Street,
She told the innkeeper she was a cousin of mine
And they served me with whiskey, with ale and
with wine. *(refrain)*

6 Soon for more whiskey I tittered and called,
The innkeeper came and shook hands with her
bold,
It was late in the evening when a cop came
around,
Says, "Assigh for such actions, please pay me
five pounds." *(refrain)*

40

cous-in to see, I fell in with a slash-er and got on a spree. Ral-di-

fal da-did-dle die-do, too-dle-i-ay

7 She paid him my money without no delay,
And then for more whiskey she sent right away.
She hired a bed and lay down by my side,
And I dreamed I was sober with a beautiful bride.　　　　　　　　　　*(refrain)*

8 My baggage she shifted while I was asleep,
And long before morning left me in the street.
I woke up without any money or clothes,
And the cop came around, saying, "You're drunk, I suppose?"　　　　　　　*(refrain)*

9 He marched me to prison with no more delay
And kept me right there till the end of the day.
He tried for to quiet me, I wouldn't keep still,
So he made me dance 'round up and down a treadmill.

10 "If you need the exercise, finish your joke!"
He made me dance there till my legs were near broke,
All the fiddlers and fifers you have at your Fair
Couldn't make me dance here like he made me dance there!　　　　　　　　　*(refrain)*

11 Before I was finished with that little jaunt
It was twenty-four guineas I begged from my aunt:
"It was up into Newport I scalded my nose
And this poor countryman lost his money and clothes.　　　　　　　　　　*(refrain)*

12 "I wish I were back in the town of Athlone
Staying close to my mother, whom I'd left at home.
You can have all your slashers, steamboats and treadmills,
For to seek out my cousin I never again will!"　　　　　　　　　　*(refrain)*

41

Seventeen Come Sunday

New Words and Music by Norman Cazden

Bonnie Annie is the name of the girl, and she doesn't come off as
well in this as in some other conversation pieces. Robert Burns was
attracted to this theme, which is not so well known in America.

1. As I walked out one May morn-ing So

ear-ly in the dawn-ing, 'Twas there I spied a pret-ty fair maid Just

2 Her shoes were bright, her stockings white,
And her buckles shining silver,
She had a dark and a rolling eye
And her hair hung over her shoulder.

(refrain)

3 She looked at me and I at her
As she tripped the grass so gaily.
I overtook her handily
And O, but she was saucy.

(refrain)

4 "Where are you going, my pretty fair maid,
And where are you going, my honey?"
She answered me most modestly,
"I'm on an errant for Granny."

(refrain)

5 "How old are you, my pretty fair maid,
How old are you, my honey?"
She answered me most modestly,
"I'm seventeen come Sunday."

(refrain)

6 "Where do you live, my pretty fair maid,
And where do you live, my honey?"
She answered me most modestly,
"In a wee house with my Granny."

(refrain)

7 "May I come along, my pretty fair maid,
May I come along, my honey?"
She answered me most modestly,
"I durst not, for my Granny."

(refrain)

8 "But you come to my Granny's house
When the wind blows keen and fairly,
And I will rise and let you in,
My Granny will not hear me."

(refrain)

9 Then I went to her Granny's house
To woo her most sincerely,
And she came tripping down the stairs
And welcomed me most cheerily.

(refrain)

10 "Can you do with a man, my pretty fair maid,
Can you do with a man, my honey?"
She answered me most modestly,
"You may come along and try me."

(refrain)

11 Then I went up with my pretty fair maid
And the wind blew keen and fairly,
And long before the gray morn came
She was not half so saucy.

(refrain)

REFRAIN

as the sun was ris - ing With my roo - ee did - dle dow,
Fal dee did - dle dow, Whack! the doo - ee did - dle die - do dow.

12 Next morning Granny took her hair
  And to the floor she brought her,
  And with the help of a hazel rod
  She thrashed one willful daughter.

  (refrain)

13 One day I met my pretty fair maid,
  "It's a cold and stormy weather."
  She answered me most modestly,
  "I am ondone forever."

  (refrain)

14 Now I have a wife in London town,
  And why should I disclaim her?
  But every town that I go in,
  I get a girl if I can gain her.

  (refrain)

The Island of Jamaica

New Words and Music by Norman Cazden

A favorite joke at the expense of the listeners, known in lumber camps of
the Northeast and nearby Canada. The tune is strikingly elaborate.

eve - ning, as I roamed a-shore from my gal - li-ant brig - an - tine On the
is - land of Ja - mai - ca, where late-ly I have been, My
mind be-ing bent on ram - bel - ling, not car - ing where I went, On-

46

to a rich plan - ta - tion my cor - ris I slow - ly bent.

2 My being tired of rambelling, I set me down to rest,
  To sing the songs of old Ireland and the home that I love best.
  Where the orange trees bedecked the fields with green and yellow buds,
  Occasionally my mind would stir with melancholy thoughts.

3 And now, my song being at an end and my mind, it being at ease,
  I arose to pick some oranges that were heavy on the trees.
  'Twas then I spied a female form, she filled me with delight,
  She wore an air of innocence, and her dress was snowy white.

4 So fresh and pure, and so demure, and her mantle it was green,
  With a silken scarf around her neck, her shoulders for to screen.
  Her hair hung down in ringellets as black as any coal,
  And her roving eye attracted me, till I did feel more bold.

5 So politely I stepped up to her, saying, "Good morning, pretty maid,"
  "And for your kind reception, good morning, sir," she said.
  Then we sat down together and we chatted for awhile,
  I told her many a hard yarn that caused her for to smile.

6 I told her that I was a sailor lad, I had lateli crossed the Main,
  The galliant ship I belonged to lay anchored in the bay.
  "And for your kind reception, I'll have you to understand
  That my name is Henry O'Ryerson, and I'm a married man.

7 "My parents live in harmony, they labor but at their ease
  While I am doing some foolishness to plow the raging seas,
  But whilst I'm doing such foolishness, to work both night and day,
  I sing the songs of old Ireland to drive my cares away.

8 " 'Twas a day before I left the shore when my troubles, they began,
  It was all about the wife I loved, she went off with some other man."
  As she arose to leave me, she made only this request,
  "Call in and see my husband, he'll treat you to the best."

9 'Twas then she introduced me to a noble-looking man.
  He kindelly saluted me and took me by the hand.
  The wine was put on the table, and the dinner was served up soon,
  We all sat down together, boys, and got drunk that afternoon!

Early One Morning

New Words and Music by Norman Cazden

The full text for this fine melody shows us
the cause for the maiden's complaint.

1. Ear-ly one morn-ing, just as the sun was ris-ing, I
heard a maid sing in the val-ley be-low:
"O, don't de-ceive me; O, nev-er leave me. How could you use a

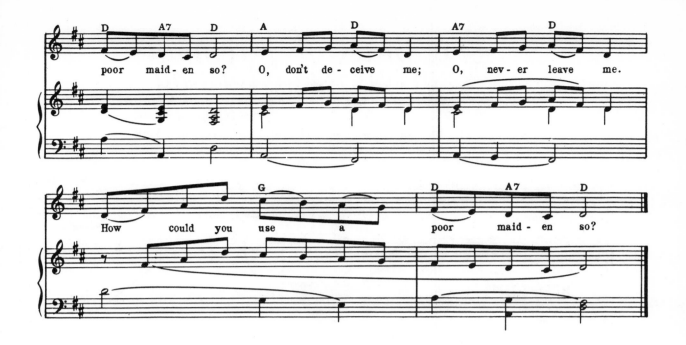

poor maid-en so? O, don't de-ceive me; O, nev-er leave me.

How could you use a poor maid-en so?

2 Remember the vows that you made to me truly,
Remember how tenderly you nestled close to me.
Gay is the garland, fresh are the roses
I've culled from the garden to bind over thee.

3 Here I now wander alone as I wonder
Why you did leave me to sigh and complain.
I ask of the roses, why should I be forsaken,
Why must I in sorrow remain?

4 Through yonder grove, by the spring that is
    running,
There you and I have so merrily played,
Kissing and courting and gently sporting:
Oh, my innocent heart you've betrayed.

5 How can you slight so a pretty girl that loves you,
A pretty girl that loves you so dearly and warm,
Though love's folly is surely but a fancy,
Still it should prove to me sweeter than your scorn.

6 Soon you will meet with another pretty maiden,
Some pretty maiden, you'll court her for awhile,
Thus ever ranging, turning and changing,
Always seeking for a girl that is new.

7 Thus sang the maiden, her sorrows bewailing,
Thus sang the maid in the valley below:
O, don't deceive me, O, never leave me,
How could you use a poor maiden so?

The Brats of Jeremiah

New Words and Music by Norman Cazden

Unhappy Jeremiah was the title of this one more than a hundred years ago, and some consolation was once offered the poor fellow, without effect. The tune belongs to some high-falutin' English ballads.

Lyrics under the staves:

1. I've oft-times heard of mar-ried life and pleas-ures with-out e-qual, So I re-solved to take a wife, yet on-ly mark the se-quel. But while my sor-rows I re-late, don't try to raise my ire; For, oh, I've of-ten cursed the fate of un-hap-py Je-re-

2 I courted Jane, the milliner; her parents were my betters,
But soon I had enough of her when bound in wedlock fetters:
There was a salesman in our town, a man she did admire,
And ofttimes she would set with him in spite of Jeremiah. *(refrain)*

3 My remonstrance was all in vain, she'd always be my master,
For if I tried to stop her tongue, it would only run the faster.
She asked this man to tea one day, she told me to retire,
I left her sitting on his knee: what a treat for Jeremiah! *(refrain)*

4 We had two children, hardly grown, and oft I had to mind them
While she would walk with other men, I had to walk behind them.
But what was more to my disgrace, O Lord, I feel on fire,
They did not look unto the face one bit like Jeremiah! *(refrain)*

5 I'd been to work quite hard one day, and to my house returning,
I found my wife had run away and all my offers spurning.
Of reason I was near bereft, folks thought I would expire,
For she had taken our goods, and left the brats for Jeremiah! *(refrain)*

51

Lolly Too-Dum

New Words and Music by Norman Cazden
This is a slight variant of a familiar
song telling of a remedy for fits.

I went out one morn-ing to breathe the morn-ing air, Lol-ly too-dum,

too - dum, lol - ly too-dum day, As I went out one morn - ing to breathe the morn-ing air, I o - ver-heard a moth - er say - ing, "Yes, my daught- er fair," Lol - ly too - dum, too - dum, Lol - ly too - dum day.

2 You better go wash those dishes and hush your chattering tongue.
Lolly too-dum, too-dum, lolly too-dum day,
I know you want to marry, but you know you are too young.
Lolly too-dum, too-dum, lolly too-dum day.

3 O, pity my condition just as you would your own . . .
For fourteen long years I have lived all alone . . .

4 Supposin' I were willing, where would you get your man? . . .
Why, Lordy mercy, mammy, I could marry handsome Sam . . .

5 Supposin' he should slight you, as you've done him before? . . .
Why, Lordy mercy, mammy, I could marry forty more . . .

6 There's peddlers and tinkers and boys from the plow . . .
O, Lordy mercy, mammy, the fit comes on me now . . .

7 O, mammy, just look at me, you can see I'm nearly grown . . .
O, Lordy mercy, mammy, just consider the case your own . . .

8 And now I am married, it's well for to be . . .
Why, ha ha ha, you jolly girls, the fit is off of me . . .

9 Well, now she is married and well for to do . . .
Now come along, you jolly boys, I'm in the market too . . .

10 With six daughters married, now who would marry you? . . .
There's no man alive would want a wife as old as you . . .

11 There's doctors and lawyers and men of all degree . . .
And some will want to marry, and some will marry me . . .

Blow The Man Down

New Words and Music by Norman Cazden

A lilting sailor's song that compares the pretty girl to a
ship, though quite unfortunately she also has a mate.

2 I will tell you a story, it's not very long,
To me way, hey, blow the man down,
It's about a young sailor bound home from
Hong-Kong,
Give me some time to blow the man down.

3 As I was a-walking down Radcliffe Highway...
A saucy young clipper I chanced for to see...

4 Her flag showed three colors, her masts they
were low...
She was round in the counter and bluff in the
bow...

5 She was bowling along with the wind blowing
free...
I slowed up my course while she waited for
me...

6 I dipped her my ensign, a signal she knew...
For she backed 'round her mainyards and hove
herself to...

7 I hailed her in English, she answered just so...
"I'm from the Blue Anchor bound to the Brown
Doe..."

54

9. We walked and we talked till I thought we were friends, To me way, hey, blow the man down; I kissed her a cou-ple and hugged her a-gain, Give me some time to blow the man down.

8 I passed her my hawser and took her in tow...
And yardarm to yardarm away we did go...

9 We walked and we talked till I thought we
were friends...
I kissed her a couple and hugged her again...

10 She turned unto me and said, "Will you stand
treat?"...
"Delighted," said I, "for a charmer so sweet."...

11 I bought her a two-shilling dinner in town...
Some trinkets and laces, a bonnet and gown...

12 In a snug little harbor we moored ourselves
down...
When the weather was right, we'd go up to
her room...

13 She treated me royally, just like a guest...
I knew if I stayed with her, I'd have the best...

14 But as we were leaving, she said unto me...
"There's a spanking full-rigger all ready for
sea!"...

15 It was just as that clipper was clear of the bar...
Her mate knocked me down with the end of
a spar...

16 So I give you fair warning, before you belay...
Never take a young Highway girl up on your
knee...

The Leather-Winged Bat

A *condensed* record of a bird convention that took place before
1656. The tune has been widely adapted for other songs.

New Words and Music by Norman Cazden

1. Hi! said the lit-tle leath-er-winged bat, I'll tell you the
rea-son that, The rea-son that I fly in the night Is be-cause I've lost my

2 Hi! said the woodpecker, sitting on a fence,
Once I courted a handsome wench,
She proved fickle and from me fled,
And ever since then my head's been red.
(refrain)

3 Hi! said the sparrow from his nest,
I loved a lass, but she thought it a jest,
And ever since that dreary spring
I've vowed that I would never sing. *(refrain)*

4 Hi! said the blackbird all in dread,
I loved one, but she has fled,
And ever since my love I lack
That is why I mourn in black. *(refrain)*

5 Hi! said the tuneful nightingale,
I have also a mournful tale,
When I sing, it's all to mourn,
For my love has left me here forlorn. *(refrain)*

6 Hi! said the little bobolink then,
I'll never be myself again,
I loved one, but I couldn't prevail,
And that is the reason I wag my tail. *(refrain)*

7 Hi! said the greenfinch as he flew,
I loved one that proved untrue,
And since she will no more be seen,
Every Spring I change to green. *(refrain)*

8 Hi! said the little chattering swallow,
My love has flown and I can't follow,
So now upon the chimney high
I sing out my poor melodie. *(refrain)*

9 Hi! said the owl, my love is gone
That I did so much dote upon,
I know not how my love to find,
But after her I whoop and whine. *(refrain)*

REFRAIN

hearts de - light, How - dee dow - dee did - dle - o - day, How - dee dow - dee

did - dle - o - day, How - dee dow - dee did - dle - o - day, With a

hey low lee le lie - lee - oh.

10 Hi! said the cardinal, chiming in,
   This is how my tale of love begins,
   I am of my dearest one bereft,
   And that's why my own country I've left.
   (refrain)

11 Hi! said the chaffinch, with barely a squeak,
   For love's sweet sorrow my heart does break,
   I grieve so for my only dear
   That I sing but two months in the year.
   (refrain)

12 Hi! said the goshawk that flies by night,
   I have lost my heart's delight,
   And ever since my love has gone away
   I never fly out in the day.   *(refrain)*

13 Hi! said the little twittering thrush,
   My plaints now begin afresh,
   For my love was so very proud,
   And that is the reason I cry aloud.
   (refrain)

14 Hi! said the pretty skylark, I
   Soar to the heavens, up so high,
   When I lost my love, it caused such pain,
   I strive to sing it away in vain.   *(refrain)*

15 Hi! said the jackdaw, I'm perplexed,
   I lost my love, so I am vexed,
   Now I'm left to lie in the straw,
   Most people still call me jackdaw.   *(refrain)*

16 Hi! said the gentle pearly linnet,
   I loved well, but her heart wasn't in it,
   Now I'm forsaken for good and all,
   Though still for naught on her I call.
   (refrain)

57

30. Hi! said the chick-a-dee, with a lit-tle squirm, Just let me find a big fat worm; I'll fly a-way up to my nest, For I have a wife I

17 Hi! said the seagull on the fly,
   I've searched the ocean and the sky,
   But I cannot find my love again,
   So I flit about in constant pain.
   (refrain)

18 Hi! said the robin, here I've stayed,
   Where once I loved a well-favored maid,
   Her beauty kindled such a spark
   That on my breast I bear the mark.
   (refrain)

19 Hi! said the raven in despair,
   Once I courted a lady fair,
   She proved fickle and turned her back,
   And ever since then I've dressed in black.
   (refrain)

20 Hi! said the meadowlark, hopping on the grass,
   I, too, loved a comely lass,
   But she wouldn't listen to her true love sing
   Though he had a voice to please a king.
   (refrain)

21 Hi! said the gaudy dressed-up jay,
   My dearest love has flown away,
   And in remembrance of my dear
   A feather of every sort I wear.
   (refrain)

22 Hi! said the hoot-owl, sitting on a limb,
   I've been to court both tall and slim,
   When I showed her a fine gold ring,
   She said she wouldn't have such a wall-eyed
      thing.
   (refrain)

23 Hi! said the eagle with his head so white,
   A lonesome day and a lonesome night,
   I thought I heard a pretty girl say
   She'd court all night and sleep all day.
   (refrain)

24 Hi! said the little turtle-dove,
   That's no way to gain his love:
   If you want to gain your heart's delight,
   You must keep him awake both day and night.
   (refrain)

25 Hi! said the oriole as he flew,
   If I was a young man, I'd choose two,
   If one didn't love me, the other one would:
   Now, don't you think my notion's good?
   (refrain)

26 Hi! said the tender mourning dove,
   I'll tell you how to gain her love,
   Court her by night and court her by day,
   Never give her time to tell you nay.
   (refrain)

REFRAIN

think's the best. How-dee dow-dee did-dle-o-day, How-dee dow dee

did-dle-o-day, How-dee dow-dee did-dle-o-day, With a hey low lee

le lie-lee oh.

27 Hi! said the cuckoo, sitting in a tree,
When I was a young man, I had three,
Two got frisky and took to flight,
And the one that's left doesn't treat me right.
(refrain)

28 Hi! said the bluebird, I'll tell you,
Once I loved a young girl too,
She wasn't sure she wanted me now,
So I got me a new string for my bow.
(refrain)

29 Hi! said the starling, high up on the barn,
I'm sure that courting can do no harm,
I fold up my wings and shrug up straight,
And I hope every young man will find a mate.
(refrain)

30 Hi! said the chickadee, with a little squirm,
Just let me find a big, fat worm,
I'll fly away up to my nest,
For I have a wife I think's the best.
(refrain)

31 Hi! said the hawk with his claws so big,
If I had a hen I'd feed like a pig,
But here I sit on a tree so high,
Which gives me good cause to wail and sigh.
(refrain)

32 Hi! said the crow unto the hawk,
I can follow your biggety talk,
You'd like to pounce and catch you a hen,
But I hope the farmer will shoot you then.
(refrain)

59

Devilish Mary

It is the tune that holds together the various elements of a song
devoted to the character of a young lady who knows her own mind.

New Words and Music by Norman Cazden

1. When I first came to town, The boys strove to be near me; Now they stay at home And seek not to ensnare me.

REFRAIN

Hi diddle lully lay, Ho, de lie lully day.

2 When I first came to town
  They brought me trifles plenty,
  Now they've changed their style
  And come with pockets empty.

  (refrain)

3 When I first came to town
  The boys called me their dearie,
  Now if you ask my name
  They call me Devilish Mary.

  (refrain)

60

4 Oh, if I was where I would be,
Then I would be where I am not,
But here I am where I must be,
And where I would be I cannot.

(refrain)

5 They say it is wrong to flirt,
They say my heart is of stone:
Why don't I speak to him kindly,
Else leave the poor boy alone? My!

(refrain)

6 They say he is only a boy,
But I know he is older than I am.
If they would leave us alone,
I only mean for to try him.

(refrain)

7 It was last night he said
That he loved me so dearly,
Called me his darling, and hoped
To live with me so cheerily.

(refrain)

8 Then I said with a smile,
"How much I regret to say no,
Here for you is a rose,
And now farewell, you must go."

(refrain)

9 I know whom I love
And I know who does love me,
I know where I'll go
And I know who'll go with me.

(refrain)

10 Through the woods we'll go
And past the boggy mire,
Straightway through the fields
Till we reach our hearts' desire.

(refrain)

11 Eyes as bright as a coal,
Lips as red as a cherry,
And it's my delight
To make the young men merry.

(refrain)

Jackie Rover

New Words and Music by Norman Cazden

This song is not very long because Jackie wastes neither
time nor opportunity. The tune somewhat resembles
The Bold Soldier.

1. On business to market, butter and cheese to buy, I
rode out a‑sing‑ing all on the did‑dle i day.

There I spied a pret - ty maid, and be - ing so in - clined, "Oh

do you want to ride a - long?" and she hopped on be - hind.

2 We rode along together, so pleasant was the scene,
   We chatted and we ambled, till we came to
       yonder green.
   As we stepped down to tarry, 'twas then I did
       espy,
   "My dearest pretty maid, that your ribbon's
       come untied."

3 She said, "Won't you be willing, and won't you
       be so kind
   To tie it up again for me?" "Dear miss, I
       wouldn't mind."
   She held wide her tender arms, and I rolled
       right between,
   Such a tying of her ribbon as never has been seen!

4 "Now, since you've been so forward, please tell
       to me your name,
   And what is your business, and wherefrom you
       came."
   "My name is Jackie Rover, I hail from Back Bay,
   I spend my time by ups and downs all on the
       diddle-i-day."

5 An hour or so we tarried, our being so inclined,
   Forgetting all our business, and never brought
       to mind,
   She looped her tender arms once more, and I
       rolled right between,
   Undid her little ribbon and tied it up again.

The Wagoner's Lad

New Words and Music by Norman Cazden

This is really an independent song, but many of its lines turn up in other songs such as *Old Smoky* and *Rye Whiskey*. The tune has also been widely borrowed.

1.Oh, I am a poor girl, my for-tune's been bad, Long time I've been court-ing the wag-on-er's lad. He court-ed me fair-ly by night and by

day, But now he has load - ed and is go - ing a - way.

2 I loved him so dearly, I thought he loved me,
But now he is leaving, he wants to be free.
"Go put up your horses and feed them some hay,
Come sit down beside me as long as you stay."

3 "My horses aren't hungry, they won't eat
   your hay,
So fare you well, darling, I'm going away."
"It's raining, it's hailing, the moon gives no light,
Your horses can't travel this dark road tonight."

4 "My horses are harnessed, my whip's in my hand,
So fare you well, darling, my horses won't stand."
"Oh, must you go and leave me to see you
   no more,
To stay here a-weeping on the wild river shore?"

5 "Your parents don't like me, they say I'm
   too poor,
They say I'm not worthy to enter your door.
Your parents are against me, and you are
   the same,
Dig down in your heart, dear, and blot out
   my name."

6 "I know they don't like you, but why should
   you care?
You know I'm your true love, you know I'm
   your dear.
I would have consented your bride for to be,
But my parents aren't willing for you to have me."

7 "I came to this city to stay for awhile,
I left my own people, it's many long miles,
You want a freeholder, and I have no land,
And that is your true love, as I understand.

8 "I work for my living, my money's my own,
And if they don't like me, they can leave me
   alone.
So early this morning when I did arise
To cross the wild river with tears in my eyes.

9 "I'm going to Georgia, I'm going to roam,
I'm going to Georgia to make it my home.
When I top this mountain, I'll look back this way,
Don't get sad and lonesome, for here I can't stay."

10 "When you reach to Georgia you'll set down
    and cry
And think of the loved one you're leaving today."
"I'll ride on to Georgia and write you my mind,
For I mean to marry and leave you behind."

11 So hard is the fortune of poor womankind,
They are always controlled and always confined,
Controlled by their parents till they are made
    wives,
Then slaves to their husbands the rest of
    their lives.

65

The West Virginia Boys

New Words and Music by Norman Cazden

It is always some neighboring state, not your own, that produces
poor quality crops of boys and other agricultural products.

1.Come, all you Vir-gin-ia girls and lis-ten to my noise: Don't you go with the West Vir-gin-ia boys, If you do, your

por - tion, it will be Corn-bread and ba - con and sas-sa-fras tea.

2 West Virginia boys a-walking down the street,
Young girls think they're looking mighty neat,
Hands in their pockets, not a dime will they find,
But how they're tickled, that poor girl is mine.

3 When they go a-courting, let me tell you where
    they go,
Over to the old man's house down below,
Young ones peeping and the old folks gone,
Girls all mad 'cause their hair's not combed.

4 First thing you know, they're a-setting on
    a chair,
First thing they say, "Has your daddy killed
    a bear?"
Next thing they say before you set down,
"Honey, can you bake your johnnycake brown?"

5 Well, they stay and they spark till it makes
    you ashamed,
Every few minutes, it's "What's your name?"
Tell you their's is Johnny, you should be
    satisfied,
Slap your knee and laugh till you're ready
    to cry.

6 They'll take you out up on the high hill,
Take you there so much against your will,
Leave you alone to weep and to rue,
For that's just the way the West Virginians do.

7 Some live in a cabin with a patch-a-log wall,
Nary a window in it at all,
Sandstone chimney and a puncheon floor,
Knotted board roof and a button-on door.

8 When they get hungry they start to make bread,
Kindle a fire as high as your head,
Rake around the ashes, and in they throw
A handful of sand they call West Virginia dough.

9 When they go to milk they milk in a gourd,
Heave it in a corner and cover it with a board,
Some get buttermilk and some get cheese,
For that is the way of the West Virgin-eye-ese.

10 When they go to farming, they have nothing
    to go on,
In February they plant a patch of corn,
The way they tend it, you wouldn't know how,
A flea-size mule and a grasshopper plow.

11 Over in the mountains where they stay
The sun doesn't shine till the middle of the day,
Foot of each mountain they have a little field,
Bushel to the acre is a very good yield.

12 When they go a-fishing, they take along a worm,
Put it on the hook just to watch it squirm,
First thing they say when they get a bite,
"I haven't caught a fish since Saturday night."

13 When they go to meeting, I'll tell you what
    they wear,
Worn tow jacket just about to tear,
Pair of cracked boots with the tops turned down,
Stringy cotton socks they wear the year 'round.

14 When you court a young man, he talks to
    you of love,
First it's "honey" and then it's "turtle dove,"
After you're married, it's no such thing,
"Get up and make my breakfast, you
    good-for-nothing thing!'

15 Brandy is brandy, no matter how you mix them,
A West Virginia boy's no better than you fix him,
When all the other folks have all gone to bed,
The devil is a-working in that boy's head.

The Maid on the Mountain's Brow

New Words and Music by Norman Cazden

A conversation piece involving strong recriminations, but without much doubt as to who will win. The unique melody is one of the most daring to be heard in the folksong tradition.

1. Come, all young men and maid-ens, come list-en to my song, I'll sing to you a verse or two, I won't de-tain you long, It's all a bout a young man I'm go-ing to tell you now,

Who had late-li fell en-am-oured of the maid on the moun-tain's brow.

2 First he says, "My pretty fair maid, you are the only one.
If I could gain your favor, from your side I never would roam."
She says, "Young men are so changeable, I'm not prepared to go,
So I'll tarry another season upon the mountain's brow."

3 Then he says, "My pretty fair maid, will you come along with me?
We'll join our hands in wedlock, it's married we will be.
It's you alone that I adore, so solemnly I do vow,
Do not tarry here no longer upon the mountain's brow."

4 Now this young and wigglesome maiden, not knowing just what to say,
Her eyes began to sparkle and so merrily she did play,
"Kind sir, I'd rather be excused, I can't go with you now,
For I must tarry another season upon the mountain's brow."

5 "Well," he says, "my pretty fair maid, I'm sure you can't say no.
Look down in yonder valley where my crops so gently grow,
Look down in yonder valley at my horses and my plow:
They are laboring late and earli for the maid on the mountain's brow."

6 "If they're at their daily labor, I'm sure it is not for me,
For I've heard of your behavior, it's none of the best, I see,
There is a place where you stop in, I've heard the people say,
Where you rap and call, and pay for all, and go home at the break of day."

7 "If I rap and call and pay for, my money is all my own,
I'll not spend of your fortune, love, for they tell me you have none.
You thought you had my poor heart won when happening onto me now,
But I can leave you where I found you upon the mountain's brow."

8 Then it's "Johnny, oh, my dearest Johnny, how can you be so unkind?
For one who loved so dearly, how quickly you've changed your mind!
There's a girl who loves you dearly, are you going to leave her now?
Don't leave her broken-hearted upon the mountain's brow!"

9 Now he hung his head in silence, not knowing just what to say,
And gazed upon the pretty fair maid who looked so neat and gay.
"You've made me here to understand, and you've consented too,
Let us tarry here no longer upon the mountain's brow."

Hi Ho, Jerum

A good Sunday School moral is wedded to a
sprightly tune, both undoubtedly of Negro origin. The
rhymes are of a type found in *Peter Gray*.

New Words and Music by Norman Cazden

1. There was a rich man and he lived in Je-ru-sa-lem,
Glo-ry hal-le-lu-jah, hi ho Je-rum. He had a fine house and he
lived ver-y spru-ci-um, Glo-ry hal-le-lu-jah, hi ho Je-rum.

REFRAIN

Hi ho Je-rum and hi ho Je-rum, Skee-dum a rink-y doo-li-um,

70

Skee-dum a rink-y doo-li-um, Glo-ry hal-le-lu-jah hi ho Je-rum.

2 Now on his doorstep stood a human wreckium,
   Glory hallelujah, hi ho Jerum.
  He wore a bowler hat, but the brim was
  'round his neckium,
   Glory hallelujah, hi ho Jerum.   *(refrain)*

3 The poor man asked for a piece of bread and
   cheesium ...
  The rich man said, "Scram, or I'll call the
  poleecium ..."   *(refrain)*

4 The poor man died and his soul went to
   Heavenium ...
  And he danced with the saints till half-past
  elevenium ...   *(refrain)*

5 The rich man died, but he didn't fare so
   wellium ...
  He couldn't reach Heaven, so he had to go
  to Hellium ...   *(refrain)*

6 He fell straight down till he got to Sheolium ...
  The Devil said, "Fine, go shovel on some
  coalium ..."   *(refrain)*

7 And now you can see why riches are no
   jokium ...
  We'll all go to Heaven, 'cause we're all stony
  brokium ...   *(refrain)*

71

The Wife
Who Was Dumb

New Words and Music by Norman Cazden

A blithe old ditty about the man who couldn't leave well enough
alone. The tune is old but not commonly associated with the song.

1. All you that pass a - long, give ear un-to my song, Con - cern-ing a youth that was young, And he loved a maid-en fair, few with her might com-pare, But a - like and a - las, she was dumb, dumb, dumb, But a - like and a -las, she was dumb.

2 She was lovely, fresh and gay like the pleasant
   flowers of May,
   And her cheeks were as round as a plum,
   She was neat in every part, she was pleasing
   to his heart,
   But alike and alas, she was dumb, dumb, dumb,
   But alike and alas, she was dumb.

3 At length this bonny blade married this pretty
   maid
   And he safeli conducted her home,
   And in her beauty bright lay all his whole delight,
   But alike and alas, she was dumb, dumb, dumb,
   But alike and alas, she was dumb.

4 Now I will plainly show what work this maid
    could do
  Which a pattern may be for girls young,
  For she did both day and night in working
    take delight,
  But alike and alas, she was dumb, dumb, dumb,
  But alike and alas, she was dumb.

5 She could knit and she could sew, she could
    bake and she could brew,
  She could sweep the house clean with a broom,
  But still the silly swain would do nothing but
    complain
  Because that his wife, she was dumb, dumb,
    dumb,
  Because that his wife, she was dumb.

6 A doctor, he lived by, and to him he did apply
  For to cure his loving wife of her mum,
  To the doctor he goes, and thus he interposed,
  "Can you make a lady speak that is dumb, dumb,
    dumb,
  Can you make a lady speak that is dumb?"

7 The doctor he did bring, and he cut her
    chattering string,
  And at liberty he set her tongue,
  When her tongue began to walk, then she began
    to talk
  As though she had never been dumb, dumb,
    dumb,
  As though she had never been dumb.

8 Her new faculty she tries, and she fills the
    house with noise,
  Till she rattles in his ears like a drum,
  And she leads him such strife, makes him weary
    of his life,
  He'd give anything at all if she was dumb, dumb,
    dumb,
  He'd give anything at all if she was dumb!

9 To the doctor then he goes and thus he
    interposed,
  Saying, "Doctor, you've got me undone,
  My wife has turned into a scold, and her
    tongue she'll never hold,
  I'd give anything at all if she was dumb, dumb,
    dumb,
  I'd give anything at all if she was dumb!"

10 Says the doctor, "For my part, it's a very easy
    art
  For to make a lady speak that is dumb,
  But you must do the best you can, it's beyond
    the art of man
  For to make a scolding woman hold her tongue,
    tongue, tongue,
  For to make a scolding woman hold her
    tongue!"

The Devil and the Farmer's Wife

New Words and Music by Norman Cazden
An uncommon and blithe variation on an old favorite theme.

1. There was an old man, he owned a small farm, He had no team to car-ry it on. Sing ra fa la, fa la, fa la-ni-go, Ray fa la, fa la-ni-go lee.

2 He hooked up his wife and his old white sow,
He plowed it all over, the Devil knows how.
(refrain)

3 One day as the farmer was going to plow,
The Devil came to him, said "How do you do?"
(refrain)

4 "I've loaned you the seed, here are horses and cart,
But with one of your family you must part."
(refrain)

5 "Oh, please don't take my eldest son,
For there's work on the farm that's got to be done."
(refrain)

74

6 "It isn't your son that I'm after now,
But your danged old wife who will have to go."
(refrain)

7 "You're welcome to have her," the old man replied,
"But if you can match her, you're worse than you're called!"
(refrain)

8 The old Devil, he got her right on to his back,
There wasn't a pedlar so fond of his pack.
(refrain)

9 But when they got to the fork of the road,
He said, "Get down, old woman, you're a hell of a load."
(refrain)

10 He set her down, for he needed a rest,
She up with a stick and hit him her best.
(refrain)

11 Then he carried her through the field of rye,
She up with her foot and kicked him in the eye.
(refrain)

12 Soon they reached Hell, and right at the door
He threw her colomicks right down on the floor.
(refrain)

13 When they got to the old fireplace,
She fell out of the sack and skun her old face.
(refrain)

14 The Devil, he said he would rest up a spell,
He wasn't married, thank Heaven, but only in Hell.
(refrain)

15 "And now that we've gotten her all to Hell,
Poke up the fire, boys, scorch her well!"
(refrain)

16 Four little devils came creeping along,
She picked up a stick and she hit every one.
(refrain)

17 Three little devils were fixing her chains,
She grabbed up a pick and she split out their brains.
(refrain)

18 "Oh now," says the Devil, "better hist her up higher."
She up with a foot and kicked two in the fire.
(refrain)

19 An old devil was laying far back on his bed,
She took up a pot and she mellered his head.
(refrain)

20 And then she kicked the young imps about,
Says one to the other, "Let's turn her out."
(refrain)

21 Nine little devils were climbing the wall
Saying, "Take her back, pappy, she'll murder us all."
(refrain)

22 The old Devil, he got her right onto his back,
And like a damned fool he went lugging her back.
(refrain)

23 Before they got within sight of home
She had tickled the skin off the Devil's backbone.
(refrain)

24 "Oh, here's your old wife, take her back for a spell,
She won't get to Heaven, and she won't stay in Hell."
(refrain)

25 "Mister Devil, you've made out mighty well,
If she'd stayed there, she'd have whipped you all out of Hell."
(refrain)

26 He says, "I've been a Devil most of my life,
But I never knew hell till I met with your wife."
(refrain)

27 And then she went whistling all over the hill,
"If the Devil won't have me, I don't know who will."
(refrain)

28 And that's where the women got the advantage of men,
They can go all to Hell and get back again.
(refrain)

Willie the Weaver

New Words and Music by Norman Cazden

This is another tale of illicit sport, somewhat like *The Jolly Boatswain*
and *The Trooper and the Tailor,* but with a surprise ending.

1. "Moth-er, moth-er, now I'm mar-ried, Don't you wish I'd long-er tar-ried? For the wom-en, they do say, Are quick to cause their men dis-may."

2 "Son, O son, now don't belabor,
But go home and dearly love her.
Give the women all their due,
And let me hear no more from you."

3 Off to home, a neighbor met him
All on purpose for to fret him.
"You won't guess, to save your life,
Who I saw a-hugging your wife.

4 "There she was with Willie the Weaver,
And they held so close together.
Saw them standing at the door,
They went in, I saw no more."

5 He reached home in mighty anger,
Knocked at the door to sound like thunder.
"Who is that?" poor Willie cried.
"That's my husband, and you must hide."

76

6 Up in the chimney Willie ventured,
   In at the door her husband entered.
   "Come, dear husband, tell me true,
   Where have you been this live-long day?

7 "You've been down at the tavern drinking,
   All your work and money lacking,
   Leaving poor me here all alone,
   But to sing and make my moan."

8 "Hush your mouth, you false deceiver,
   Where have you hid that Willie the Weaver?"
   "Search the house and all around,
   There won't be any Willie found."

9 He looked about the house twice over,
   Saw no place where Willie took cover.
   In the fireplace, print of a boot,
   Falling down some bits of soot.

10 "Well, my lad, I'm glad I found you,
   I won't hang and I won't drown you."
   This he thought, but nothing spoke,
   Meaning to stifle him with smoke.

11 He built up a rousing fire,
   So to please his strong desire,
   Made poor Willie cough and sneeze,
   And in that place he found no ease.

12 He put on more blazing fuel,
   Till up spoke his dearest jewel,
   "If I am your loving wife,
   Take him down and spare his life!"

13 Down from the chimney he roughly took him,
   'Cross the floor he fairly shook him,
   Mauled his face and clothes likewise
   And sent him home with two black eyes.

14 "Willie the Weaver is gone to stay,
   And he won't bother you night or day,
   But while you keep on with me here,
   What have you to say, my dear?"

15 "Once I've told you, twice I've told you,
   If you're not pleased by what I do,
   Tell you over a thousand times,
   Just you move on down the line!"

Won't You Sit With Me Awhile?

New Words and Music by Norman Cazden

Some most mature questions about human relations
are fitted here to a very expressive melody.

1. As I walked out one May morn- ing, I met with a nice young girl. I said to her, "My pret- ty fair miss, Won't you sit with me a while?"

2 "Oh no, kind sir," she answered me,
   "Oh no, I can't sit down,
   I can't sit with you by the river's side,
   Oh Lord, I am too young."

3 "The younger that you are, my dear,
   The better 'twill be for me,
   For I vow and I do declare
   I will wed no woman but thee."

4 He courted her with compliments
   Till she didn't know her mind,
   He courted her with so merry a mood,
   Till he got her to comply.

5 He took her by her gentle hand,
   He kissed her cheek and chin,
   Then he took her up to his bedroom
   To stay awhile with him.

6 All in the first part of the night
   They both did sport and play,
   And all the latter part of that night
   Close in his arms she lay.

7 The night being gone and the day coming on,
   The daylight shining clear,
   This young man rose, put on his clothes,
   Saying, "Fare you well, my dear."

8 "Oh, are those the kind words you said to me
   When your head lay upon my breast?
   You made me believe by your false tongue
   That the sun rose in the west."

9 "Go home to your father's garden,
   Sit down and cry your fill,
   And when you think on what you have done,
   You may blame your own goodwill."

10 "Is that the promise you made to me
    Down by the river's side?
    You vowed and declared you would marry me
    And make me your lawful bride."

11 "I vowed to wed no other than you,
    And I'll marry with none, I know,
    For I cannot wed with anyone
    So easily won as you."

12 There's a herb in my father's garden
    And some do call it rue,
    When fishes fly and swallows swim,
    Then young men will prove true.

13 There is many a farmer's daughter
    To the market she does go,
    While I, poor girl, must stay to home
    For to rock the cradle, O.

14 To rock the cradle, O, my dear,
    And sing the baby bye,
    Was ever a maid in all the world
    So carelessly won as I?

15 Come, all you fair and handsome girls,
    A warning take by me,
    Don't ever trust your own true love
    One inch above your knee.

16 He'll hug you close and he'll kiss you thus,
    He will roll you all about,
    Then he'll leave you as mine has left me
    To wheel the baby out.

17 There's light into the stars above,
    There's soft green grass below,
    There's many a cry will stay upon a man
    For serving a poor girl so.

Michael Finnigin

New Words and Music by Norman Cazden

The troubles of the unfortunate Michael are mainly those of finding good rhymes. The melody does not often follow so appropriate a circular pattern.

1. There once was a man named Mi-chael Fin-ni-gin, He grew whisk-ers on his chin-ni-gin, The wind came up and blew them in-ni-gin, Poor old Mi-chael

2 There once was a man named Michael Finnigin,
He got drunk from too much ginnigin,
So he wasted all his tinnigin,
Poor old Michael Finnigin. (Beginnigin)

Fin - ni - gin (Be - gin - ni -gin!)

3 There once was a man named Michael Finnigin,
   He kicked up an awful dinnigin
   Because they said he must not sinnigin,
   Poor old Michael Finnigin. (Beginnigin)

4 There once was a man named Michael Finnigin,
   He went fishing with a pinnigin,
   Caught a fish but he dropped it innigin,
   Poor old Michael Finnigin. (Beginnigin)

5 There once was a man named Michael Finnigin,
   Climbed a tree and barked his shinnigin,
   Took off several yards of skinnigin,
   Poor old Michael Finnigin. (Beginnigin)

6 There once was a man named Michael Finnigin,
   He grew fat and he grew thinnigin,
   Then he died, and we have to beginnigin,
   Poor old Michael Finnigin. (Beginnigin)

The Jolly Boatswain

New Words and Music by Norman Cazden

2 As she was out a-walking down along the street,
The handsome little tailor she chanced for to meet.
She said, "My jolly boatswain is going off to sea,
If you have no other place, you can lodge along
with me."   (refrain)

3 The tailor lad came early the boatswain's wife
to see,
They kissed and canoodled as happy as could be,
It wasn't very long 'fore they turned out the light
And they had a merry time of it so early in the
night.   (refrain)

4 'Bout ten o'clock or more came a rapping at the
door,
This little tailor lad couldn't sleep any more.
Said the tailor to the wife, who was still half
asleep,
"I hear your jolly boatswain, now where will I
creep?"   (refrain)

5 Said the wife to the tailor, being half undressed,
"I don't know a place, only over in that chest."
She put him in the chest among a lot of other
things,
Then she ran down the stairs for to let her
husband in.   (refrain)

82

One of several related song strains which include *The Charleston Merchant,*
The Trooper and the Tailor, Willie the Weaver and some other jests. In
this particular form we are left to wonder what the
boatswain needs with such a mess of tea.

sea, A frol-ic with the tail-or lad the boat-swain's wife did play. Fal di rod-dy, too la rod-dy, Fal di rod-dy too la ray.

6 She wrapped herself around and unbolted the
    door,
There stood her husband with seven sailors more.
She hugged him and kissed him and gave him
    caresst,
Said she, "Dearest husband, what's the meaning
    of all this?"   *(refrain)*

7 "I haven't come to 'sturb you, nor rob you of
    your rest,
But I'm going off to sea and I've come to get
    my chest."
He went on up the stairs with his seven sailors
    strong,
They grabbed right aholt and they yanked it
    right along.   *(refrain)*

8 They hadn't gotten more than halfway through
    the town
'Fore the heft of the chest caused the sweat to
    run down.
They went a little further and sot them down
    to rest,
Said one to the other, "What the devil's in that
    chest?"   *(refrain)*

9 The boatswain turned the hasps and lifted up
    the lid:
There sot the little tailor lad a-scratching on his
    head.
So they took him down to Chiny and traded him
    for tea,
And they had enough tea for to serve your
    company.   *(refrain)*

I Was There

New Words and Music by Norman Cazden

Good lies are always well-appreciated, for they require brains and a firm
honesty to be effectively brash. The misinformation here serves us right
if we haven't learned our history any better than this.

1. I was born al-most ten thou-sand years a - go,
And there's hard-ly an-y-thing that I don't know.
I saw Pe-ter, Paul and Mo-ses play-ing ring a-round the

2 I'm a very highly educated man,
And it's hard to keep my knowledge all to hand,
I have lived on earth so long
That I used to sing this song
When Abraham and Isaac made their plan.

3 I saw Adam and Eve driven from the door,
I'm the fellow picked the fig-leaves that they
wore,
I was 'round the corner peeping
While that apple they were eating,
I can prove that I'm the one who ate the core.

4 I saw Cain and Abel playing in the shade,
And I'm sure that it was poker that they played,
But there's just one little rub:
Did he hit him with a club?
I thought it was a diamond or a spade.

5 I sold spearheads in the Neolithic Age,
And I trained a dinosaurus for the stage,
But when I first made a fire
And a wheel without a tire,
Then my cave received a lot of patronage.

6 I was there when Noah built his famous Ark,
And I crawled in through a window after dark.
I saw old Pharoah's daughter
Fishing Moses from the water,
Then I crossed the land of Canaan for a lark.

7 I saw Pharoah being pestered by the fleas,
I helped Brigham Young invent limburger cheese,
And while sailing down the bay
With Methusaleh one day,
I saved his flowing whiskers from the breeze.

84

ro - ses, And I'll lick an - y - one who says it is - n't so.

8 Oh, I used to whittle toothpicks for King Saul,
  And I clubbed that big Goliath with a maul,
  While the son of Priam swore
  And the Trojans all got sore,
  I danced around with Helen on the wall.

9 I saw Jonah when he embarked within the whale
  And he never thought he'd live to tell the tale,
  But I told Jonah to eat some garlic,
  Which gave the whale a colic,
  So he coughed him up and let him out on bail.

10 I saw Samson when he laid the village cold,
   I saw Daniel tame the lions in the hold,
   I helped them build the Tower of Babel
   Up as high as they were able,
   And there's lots of other things I haven't told.

11 Did you know that I had built the Parthenon
   Where Euripedes declared, "Well, I swan!"
   And I used to serve the teas
   For my friend Praxiteles
   While Pie-lato served us from his demijohn.

12 When I sailed with Cleopatra on the Nile,
   She whispered to me, with a touching smile,
   "Now, don't fret about that Tony,
   For you know he is a phony,
   And I've really been stuck on you all the while."

13 I saw Nero fiddling while he burned·up Rome,
   And it looked like he might have a mess at home,
   But he had the nerve to swear,
   So I dragged him from the chair,
   And I broke a bottle of lager on his dome.

14 I was present when King Alfred burned the cake.
   That was lucky, or his stomach would have ached.
   And while Robert watched the spider
   As I sat there drinking cider,
   I convinced him Christian Science was a fake.

15 Queen Elizabeth, she fell in love with me,
   We were married in Milwaukee secretly,
   But I turned around and shook her,
   I went off with General Hooker
   To shoot mosquitoes down in Tennessee.

16 Oh, I made a face at Empress Josephine
   And regret to state the fact that I was seen,
   So I fought at break of day
   With Napoleon, and say,
   I shot him through the goozle with a bean.

17 If you don't believe that all I say it true,
   Well, what difference does it really make to you?
   I'm just handing you this line
   For to pass away the time,
   And now I'm going to quit, because I'm through.

Simple Little Nancy Brown

New Words and Music by Norman Cazden

A teasing song making clever use of the refrain. The
tune derives from *London Bridge Is Falling Down.*

1. Sim - ple lit - tle Nan - cy Brown from 'way down East come in - to town; She
2. They went walk - ing by the beach, They went in swim - ming, got out of reach; She

went to see a cir - cus show And met a nice young man you know.
lost her socks and ev - 'ry - thing. So, what d'ye sup - pose she came home in?

REFRAIN

La tide - lee ide - lee - um, Tide - lee ide - lee ide - lee - um,

La tide - lee ide - lee - um, The fire - works were love - ly.
She came home in the twi - light.

86

I Wish I Was A Single Girl

New Words and Music by Norman Cazden

Considering all the possibilities, when mistaken marriages
are made, the woman is likely to have the worst of it.

1. When I was sin-gle, mar-ry-ing was my crave, Now I am mar-ried, and I'm trou-bled to my grave, And it's oh, Lord, I wish I was a sin-gle girl a-gain.

2 When I was single, I lived at my ease,
Now I am married, with a husband to please...
(refrain)

3 When I was single, went dressed up so fine,
Now I am married, go ragged all the time...
(refrain)

4 When I was single, ate biscuit and pie,
Now I am married, it's eat corn-bread or die...
(refrain)

5 When I was single, my shoes, they were new,
Now I am married, the water runs right through...
(refrain)

6 Dishes to wash and the spring to go to,
No one to help me, I have it all to do...
(refrain)

7 Two little children, mine to maintain,
Neither one big enough to do anything...
(refrain)

8 Two little children lying in one bed,
Both of them so hungry, they can't raise up their
heads...   *(refrain)*

9 If I could just go back seven long years,
I'd push back my bonnet and wipe away the
tears...   *(refrain)*

Lavender's Blue

New Words and Music by Norman Cazden
A nursery-school favorite when the text is shortened;
we do not always learn what actions of a king and
queen are being told, nor what the refrain means.

1. Lav - en - der's blue, did - dle did - dle, Lav - en - der's green,
When I am king, did - dle did - dle, You shall be queen.

2 Lavender's green, diddle diddle,
Lavender's blue,
You must love me, diddle diddle,
'Cause I love you.

3 James goes to town, diddle diddle,
Sue to the farm,
He keeps a maid, diddle diddle,
She sees her man.

4 But if by chance, diddle diddle,
They should be found?
Therefore in haste, diddle diddle,
They roll around.

5 Your neighbor's maid, diddle diddle,
Her name was Nell,
She was a lass, diddle diddle,
That I loved well.

6 But if she die, diddle diddle,
By some mishap,
Then let her lie, diddle diddle,
Under the tap.

7 That she may drink, diddle diddle,
When she is dry,
Because she loved, diddle diddle,
My dog and I.

8 Call on your friends, diddle diddle,
Let them to sport,
Some to make hay, diddle diddle,
None to report.

9 Some to the field, diddle diddle,
Some to hoe corn,
While you and I, diddle diddle,
Keep the bed warm.

10 I heard a bird, diddle diddle,
Sing in my ear,
Maids will be scarce, diddle diddle,
Come the new year.

11 For young men are, diddle diddle,
So careless grown,
That they don't mind, diddle diddle,
Which is their own.

12 Down in the vale, diddle diddle,
   Where flowers grow,
   And the birds sing, diddle diddle,
   All in a row.

13 A brisk young man, diddle diddle,
   Met with a maid,
   And laid her down, diddle diddle,
   Under the shade.

14 There they did play, diddle diddle,
   And kiss and court,
   All the fine day, diddle diddle,
   Making good sport.

15 I've heard them say, diddle diddle,
   Since I came hither
   That you and I, diddle diddle,
   Might lie together.

16 Therefore be kind, diddle diddle,
   While here we lie
   And you will love, diddle diddle,
   My dog and I.

17 For you and I, diddle diddle,
   Now all are one,
   And we will lie, diddle diddle,
   No more alone.

18 Lavender's blue, diddle diddle,
   Lavender's green,
   Let me be king, diddle diddle,
   You be the queen.

19 Lavender's green, diddle diddle,
   Lavender's blue,
   You must love me, diddle diddle,
   'Cause I love you.

Kate and her Horns

New Words and Music by Norman Cazden

A carefully worded tale by which a wise young maid takes fair
advantage of a knave. The tune seems unknown for this song, but
similar tunes have been used for the ballad *Lord Bateman*.

1.You that in mer-ri-ment de-light, Pray lis-ten un-to what I re-cite, So
shall you sat-is-fact-ion find, 'Twill cure a me-lan-chol-y mind.

2 A damsel fair lived in Colchester,
  At length a clothier courted her
  For six month's apace, both night and day,
  And yet the damsel still said nay.

3 She said, "Were I to love inclined,
  Perhaps you soon might change your mind
  And court some other damsel fair,
  For men are false, I do declare."

4 He many protestations made,
  And like a loyal lover said,
  "There's none but you shall be my wife,
  The joy and comfort of my life."

5 At length this maid gave her consent
  To marry him, and straight they went
  Unto their parents then, and who
  Both gave their leave and their liking, too.

6 But see the cursèd fruits of gold!
  He left his loyal love, to hold
  Her grief and sorrow all compassed round,
  While he a greater fortune found.

7 A lawyer's daughter fair and bright,
  Her parent's joy and whole delight,
  He was resolved to make his spouse,
  Denying all his former vows.

8 And when poor Kate came this to hear,
  That she might lose her only dear
  All for the lawyer's daughter's sake,
  Some sport of him Kate thought she'd make.

90

11. Kate to a lone-some path did stray, At length the cloth-ier came that way, And he was sore - ly scared of her, She looked so like old Luc - i - fer.

9 Kate knew each and every night he came
From his new love, Nancy by name,
Sometimes at ten o'clock, or more.
Kate to a tanner went, therefore.

10 She borrowed there an old cowhide
With crooked horns both large and wide,
And when she'd wrapped herself therein,
Her new intrigue she did begin.

11 Kate to a lonesome path did stray.
At length the clothier came that way,
And he was sorely scared of her,
She looked so like old Lucifer.

12 With hairy hide, horns on her head
That near three feet asunder spread,
He strove to run, but his feet did fail,
And then he saw her long, black tail.

13 Kate quickly seized him by the throat,
And with grim voice and a doleful note,
She said, "You leave poor Kate, I hear,
To wed the lawyer's daughter dear.

14 "Since you have been so false to her,
You perjured knave of Colchester,
You shall, whether you will or no.
Into my gloomy regions go."

15 This voice did sore affright him,
And, kneeling on his trembling limbs,
Cried, "Master Devil, spare my life,
And I will make dear Kate my wife.

16 "I'll make young Kate my lawful bride."
"See that you do," the Devil cried,
"If Kate against you does complain,
You soon will hear from me again."

17 Then home he went, though very late,
He little thought that it was Kate
That set him all in such affright,
Therefore, next day, by morning light,

18 He went to Kate and he married her
For fear of doleful Lucifer.
Kate's friends and parents thought it strange
That there was such a sudden change.

19 Kate never let her parents know,
Nor any other person too,
Till they a year had married been,
She told it at her lying-in.

20 It pleased the women to the heart,
They said she'd fairly played her part
Her husband laughed just as well as they,
It was a merry and a happy day.

91

The Bold Grenadier

New Words and Music by Norman Cazden

Most often known as *The Nightingale's Song,* the double meanings are not always appreciated. This tune is unique.

I went a-walk-ing one morn-ing in May, I spied a fair cou-ple as they were at play. One was a la-dy, a la-dy so fair, T'

92

o - ther a sol - dier, a bold gren - a - dier. Rat-tle- ee, rat - tle - o, T' o - ther a sol - dier, a bold gren - a - dier.

2 Says he, "Comeli fair maid, will you go along
    with me
  'Neath the banks of prim lilies, where the wild
    rose grows high?
  We will set ourselves down by the first rising
    stream
  To hear the lark whistle and the nightingale sing,
    Rattle-ee, rattle-o,
  To hear the lark whistle and the nightingale sing."

3 With such conversation they walked on together,
  And where for to walk when they could not tell
    whether?
  They sat themselves down by the first rising
    stream
  And they heard the lark whistle and the
    nightingale sing.
    Rattle-ee, rattle-o,
  And they heard the lark whistle and the
    nightingale sing.

4 He gently embraced the fair maid 'round her
    middle
  And out of his pack sack he pulled forth a fiddle.
  He played her a tune, caused the valley to ring,
  And it sounded more sweet than the nightingale
    sings.
    Rattle-ee, rattle-o,
  And it sounded more sweet than the nightingale
    sings.

5 "Now," says the soldier, "it's time to leave o'er."
  "Oh no," says the fair maid, "a tune or two more!"
  So he keyed up his fiddle all on the high string
  And he played her the same tune right over
    again.
    Rattle-ee, rattle-o,
  And he played her the same tune right over
    again.

6 "Now," says the fair maid, "you must marry me."
  "Oh no," says the soldier, "that never can be,
  For I have a wife in my own counteree,
  And a handsomer damsel you'll scarce ever see.   "
    Rattle-ee, rattle-o,
  And a handsomer damsel you'll scarce ever see."

7 Now come all you pretty fair maids, take
    warning from me,
  Don't place your affections on a young man so
    free,
  For he will ondo you, as mine has done me,
  And he'll leave you alone to sing bye-o-baby.
    Rattle-ee, rattle-o,
  And he'll leave you alone to sing bye-o-baby.

My Ducksie Has Fled

New Words and Music by Norman Cazden

Few so innocent as a sailor lad, when his ducksie is gone he is painfully sad. He'll find another, but not likely with so lyrical a tune, which seems mournful only in a major key.

1. As I went a-walk-ing on a fair sum-mer's day In Lon-don's fair ci-ty, there I chanced for to spy A hand-some young duck-sie, so mod-est and so true, With her cheeks like two ros-es and her cloth-ing so gay.

94

2 "I will not, I shall not, I should not go with you,
   I dare not go with you, for I'm much afeared
   My parents will be angry to see so fair a maid
   Falling in with such a lovyer, a sailor besides."

3 Kind kisses I gave her with eager intend
   With so comely a fair maid some pleasures to
      spend.
   Five guineas she asked, and the money soon had,
   And our supper being over, we went up to bed.

4 We sported and toyed till the morning drew near,
   Enjoyed my young ducksie and called her my
      dear.
   The sport being over, I started to nod,
   She picked over my pockets, took all that I had.

5 I turned 'round to kiss her, and instantly found
   A large bolster beside and a pillow on the ground.
   She had plundered and robbed me and taken
      all I had
   And she left me to wonder where my ducksie
      has fled.

95

The Old Maid's Lament

New Words and Music by Norman Cazden

A patter song using an old jig tune, and suggesting a highly theatrical
pretence, rather than a personal plea. Few of the occupations listed would
appeal to a present-day maid, even after she had passed twenty-six.

1. Come all you pret-ty maid-ens, some old and some young-er, You all have your sweet heart's, while I must wait long-er, Some six-teen, some eight-een, and some late-ly mar-ried And all well en-joy-ing your-selves while I tar-ried. A

REFRAIN

pin-man, a tin-man, a tink-er, a tail-or, A fid-dler, a ped-lar, a plow-boy, a sail-or, Come gen-tle, come sim-ple, come fool-ish, come wit-ty, If you lack a maid, come and take me a-way.

2 I am seemly fair, if my glass do not flatter,
Yet by the effects, there is something the matter,
For everyone else can have suitors a-plenty,
Most marry at sixteen, but I am past twenty.
(refrain)

3 I've often observed, and it makes me to wonder,
That many have sweethearts at fifteen and under,
And if they pass sixteen, they think their time wasted,
Oh, what shall I do when so long I have lasted?
(refrain)

4 I have a sister Susan, though pale and mis-shapen,
Before she was sixteen years old, she was taken,
Before she was eighteen, had a son and a daughter,
While I'm six-and-twenty with never an offer!
(refrain)

5 I use all the motives my sex will permit me
To put men in mind, that they may not forget me,
I've lately improved both my hair and my dentures,
Yet do what I will, there is never a man ventures.
(refrain)

6 I never will scold and I'll never be jealous,
I'll give my husband money to spend at the alehouse,
And while he's there spending, I'll be home a-saving:
Now, let the world judge if I'm not worth the having!
(refrain)

7 Whoever he be that will ease my affliction
And cast upon me an auspicious affection
Shall find me so tractable, so to content him,
That he of his bargain will never repent him.
(refrain)

The Roving Pedlar

New Words and Music by Norman Cazden

These adventures are also known to have befallen a roving gambler and
a roving Irishman. But the tune is generally an unknown bit of whimsy.

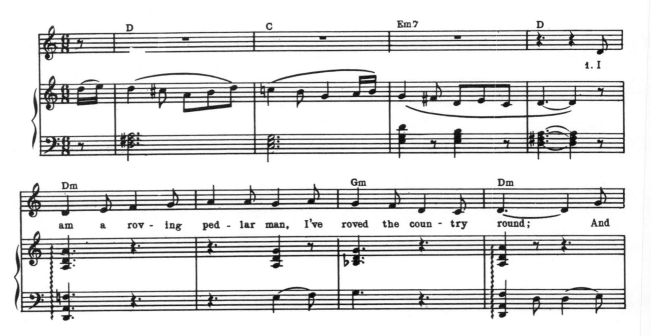

am a rov-ing ped-lar man, I've roved the coun-try round; And

2 When I came to New Hampshire, the girls all
  laughed for joy,
  The one says to the other, "There's that handsome
  pedlar boy!"
  They invited me to dine with them, they took
  me by the hand,
  And the toasts, they did fly merrily, "Success to
  the pedlar man!"

3 I went to Hillsboro County, and there among
  the maids,
  With my bold conversation they seemed not
  dismayed,
  While I such fine things sold them, gave them
  to understand
  The humor and good nature of this roving
  pedlar man.

4 It's in that Hillsboro County where the girls all
  dress so neat,
  They are kind in every feature and their kisses
  are so sweet,
  There's handsome Jane and Sally, and fair young
  Betsy too,
  Along with one of these fair maids I'll rove the
  country through.

5 I went into a tavern, and there all night I stayed,
  The landlady's fair daughter of me was not afraid,
  She hugged me and she kissed me too, she held
  me by the hand,
  And shyly told her mamma that she loved this
  pedlar man.

when I was re-solv-ed to view some oth-er ground, With my pack up-on my shoul-der and my cudg-el in my hand, I went in-to New Hamp-shire to view that hand-some land.

6 "O daughter, dearest daughter, what do you mean to do?
To rove about the country with a man that you don't know?"
"O mamma, I don't care for that, so do the best you can,
For I'll roam the country over with this roving pedlar man."

7 It was early in the morning when I was going away,
The landlady's fair daughter to me these words did say,
"How can you be so cru-el, or prove to me unkind,
To go once more a-roving and to leave me here behind?"

8 Now I'll leave off my peddling and I'll take to me a wife,
For along with this pretty girl I'll surely spend my life.
I'll embrace here late and early, and do the best I can
To cause her for to bless the day she wed the pedlar man.

The Flat River Raftsman

New Words and Music by Norman Cazden

The people in this song were real, but the story is a piece of pure
fiction with ulterior motives and extravagant language.

1. I'm a heart-brok-en rafts-man, from Green-ville I came, All
mirth is de-part-ed, from all joys I'll re-frain; From the small darts of Cu-pid that
gave me such grief, My heart breaks a-sund-er, I'll ne'er get re-lief.

2 My occupation's a-rafting where the Flat River
   rolls,
   My name is engraved on the rocks and sand
   shoals;
   Through shops, bars and households I'm very
   well known,
   They call me Jack Haggerty, the pride of the
   town.

3 I'll tell you my troubles without no more delay:
   A bright little lassie my heart stole away;
   She's a blacksmith's daughter on the Flat River's
   side,
   And I always intended to make her my bride.

100

4 Her neck's like a doughnut, both slender and neat;
Her hair hung in ringlets to her tiny white feet;
Her voice was as clear as the nightingale's song,
It rang in my ears all the day and night long.

5 I took her to suppers, to parties and balls,
Sunday boat-riding, our first early calls;
She told me she loved me as we stole through the town,
And her voice was as clear as the rise of the morn.

6 I dressed her in muslin, silk, satin and lace;
With the costliest of jewels her hands I embraced;
I gave her my wages each month, to keep safe,
Begrudged her of nothing I had on the earth.

7 I worked on the river and earned quite a stake,
Steadfast and steady, I ne'er played the rake;
I was thrillèd and happy on the burning white stream,
The thought of sweet Anna haunted my dreams.

8 One day, on the river, a letter I received:
She told me from her promise herself she'd relieved
To marry a loved one she'd long time delayed;
Next time that I saw her, she'd ne'er be a maid.

9 Her mother, Jane Tucker, was the one I had blamed,
Caused her to leave me and slandered my name,
To cast off the riggings that God would soon tie,
She left me to wander till the day that I die.

10 Farewell to Flat River, for me there's no rest,
I'll shoulder my peavey and I will go west,
I'll go to Montana, some comfort to find,
I'm leaving Flat River and sweet Anna behind.

11 Come all you bold raftsmen, kindhearted and true,
Don't trust a woman, you're beat if you do!
If ever you see one with a brown, chestnut curl,
Just think of Jack Haggerty and his Flat River girl.

I Wish
I Was Single Again

New Words and Music by Norman Cazden

The familiar situation here reaches us with an unusual melody and a
highly bewitching refrain that tends to grow on us with repetition.

1. I wish I was sin-gle a-gain, a-gain, I wish I was sin-gle a-gain, dear; For when I was sin-gle, my pock-ets did jin-gle, And I wish I was sin-gle a-gain, dear. Oh, Nan-cy O, my Nan-cy O, Oh Nan-cy, where have you been? I've

102

been to hear the lit-tle birds sing, It's all on a sum-mer's morn-ing.

2 Again and again and again, again,
Again and again and again, dear,
For when I was single, my pockets did jingle,
And I wish I was single again, dear. *(refrain)*

3 Oh, when I was single, why then, why then,
Oh, when I was single, why then, dear,
I lived at my ease and I did what I pleased,
And I wish I was single again, dear.   *(refrain)*

4 I married a wife and it's then, oh then,
I married a wife and it's then, dear,
I had nothing but strife, she's the plague of
    my life,
And I wished I was single again, dear. *(refrain)*

5 My wife, she did scold me and then, and then,
My wife, she did scold me and then, dear,
Whatever she told me made my blood run cold,
And I wished I was single again, dear. *(refrain)*

6 My wife, she got angry, and then, and then,
My wife, she got angry, and then, dear,
She beat me, she banged me, she swore she
    would hang me,
And I wished I was single again, dear. *(refrain)*

7 She beat me so hard that it's then, oh then,
She beat me so hard that it's then, dear,
I fled to the garden to repent of my bargain,
How I wished I was single again, dear. *(refrain)*

8 But then I was clever, for then, for then,
But then I was clever, for then, dear,
My wife took a fever, and I hated to leave her,
But I wished I was single again, dear. *(refrain)*

9 I came to her side again, again,
I came to her side again, dear,
When I found she had died, and I laughed
    till I cried
To think I was single again, dear.   *(refrain)*

10 She wasn't so loud right then, right then,
She wasn't so loud right then, dear,
When I went for her shroud, and I felt
    mighty proud:
To be sure, I was single again, dear. *(refrain)*

11 She didn't scold often right then, right then,
She didn't scold often right then, dear,
When I went for the coffin, I almost died
    laughin'
To think I was single again, dear.   *(refrain)*

12 She was buried next day and then, and then,
She was buried next day, and then, dear,
The music did play and I danced all the way,
I was glad to be single again, dear.   *(refrain)*

13 I walked out alone at last, at last,
I walked out alone at last, dear,
And I spied a fine lass, her eyes shone like
    glass,
I was glad to be single again, dear.   *(refrain)*

14 So I married me another, oh then, oh then,
So I married me another, oh then, dear,
She's worse than the other, she's the Devil's
    grandmother,
I wish I was single again, dear.   *(refrain)*

15 Again and again and again, again,
Again and again and again, dear,
For when I was single, my pockets did jingle,
And I wish I was single again, dear.   *(refrain)*

Down By The Greenwood Shady

New Words and Music by Norman Cazden

The very distinctive melody for this version of *The Cruel Mother* produces
some surprising shocks by under-playing some of the lines of text.

1. There was a maid-en lived in New York, Ho - ly and lone - ly, There
was a maid-en lived in New York, She was court - ed by her
fa - ther's clerk Down by the green - wood sha - dy.

2 It fell once upon a holiday,
  Holy and lonely,
  It fell once upon a holiday,
  The clerk and the maiden went to play
  Down by the greenwood shady.

3 She was passing through her father's corn...
  It's there she had two pretty babes born...

4 She leaned her back against an oak...
  At first it bent and then it broke...

5 She laid her head against a stone...
  And there most bitterly did moan...

6 She had nothing to wrap them in...
  But her old apron, and that was thin...

7 She had a penknife keen and sharp...
  She pierced it through their tender little
    hearts...

8 She took a ribbon from her hair...
  And bound their bodies fast and sure...

9 She had four fingers long and slim...
  She dug a hole and she put them in....·

10 She washed her penknife in the brook...
   The more she washed, the redder it looked...

11 She wiped her hands all on the clay...
   And thought to wipe the stain away...

12 One day she passed through her father's
     fields...
   And there she saw two babes playing ball...

13 "Oh babes, oh babes, if you were mine...
   I'd dress you in a silk so fine..."

14 "Oh cruel mother, we babes can tell...
   We know your soul and your deeds so well..."

The Little Cabin Boy

New Words and Music by Norman Cazden
A rare and tragic tale of a lady so gay who couldn't
convince the Captain that she was serious.

1.'Tis of a la - dy so gay And poss-essed of beau-ty bright.

2 Away onto Billy she's gone.
"Will you stay on the shore with me?
For my affections, they are so great,
My mind is fixed onto thee."

3 "If your affections are so great,
Mine are greater still,
But first your must go to the captain of the ship
And gain his right goodwill."

4 Then away to the captain she's gone,
"Oh captain, coo," cried she,
"I have a request to ask of thee,
And I hope you will grant it to me."

5 "Ask on, ask on, lady gay,
For what can be pleasing to thee?"
"Can little Billy, your little cabin boy,
Can he tarry on the shore with me?"

6 "What, an' you are a lady so gay,
And you've asked me for my boy?
More fittin', it would be for some rich lords and
knights
Your fair body to enjoy."

7 "No matter for that," cried she,
Will you not grant me my will?
Then a silent funeral you must prepare,
For a lady gay you will kill."

106

All for the sake of a lit-tle cab-in boy, She for-saked both lords and knights.

8 "Go 'way with your foolish yarns,
And come no more unto me,
For little Billy, my little cabin boy,
Cannot tarry on the shore with thee."

9 Away onto Billy she's gone
With a wet and a watery eye,
Saying, "The nearest and dearest of friends must
    part,
And so must you and I."

11 Going out in the garden that night
And throwing herself on the ground,
Early, early when the men arose,
Her lamenting corpse they found.

12 Her father, being a sorrowful man,
Layed aside all joys and mirth,
A silent grave he did then prepare
For to put her under the earth.

13 Now Billy's on the salt water sea,
And the waves toss, to and fro,
Lamenting like a little turtle-dove
Wherever the wind does blow.

14 Till at length a storm did arise
And the ship was out to the sea,
The captain and Billy and the merry men were
    lost,
Never more to be heared or seen.

Black
Is The Color

New Words, Adaptation and New Music by Norman Cazden

Here is the original meaning of the song, a complaint by a girl about the perfidy of men. The melodic contour is unusual but fitting.

1. Black is the col-or of my true love's hair, His lips are like some ro-sy fair, The pret-ti-est face and the neat-est hands, I love the ground where — on he stands.

2 I love my love, and well he knows
I love the grass whereon he goes.
If you no more on earth I'll see,
I can't serve you as you've served me.

3 I'll climb up high to mourn and weep,
For satisfied I'll never sleep.
You have turned away and broken my heart:
Oh, how can I from you depart?

4 Yes, you are all for this to blame,
That I must lie in grief and shame,
For you have left me lying alone
To think of what for me you've done.

5 Many a night I've been with you
And never thought you were not true.
When I found out, I cried aloud,
Such faithless love as you followed!

6 The winter is past, and the leaves are green,
The time is gone that we have seen;
But still I longed for the day to come
When you and I would be as one.

7 My own true love, oh, fare you well,
Our love has gone, but I wish you well,
Your face no more on earth I'll see,
And my life will quickly fade away.

8 Black, black is the color of my true love's hair,
His lips are like some rosy fair,
The prettiest face and the neatest hands,
I love the ground whereon he stands.

Bible Stories

New Words and Music by Norman Cazden

These new interpretations of well-known events bring remote meanings close and so are truly reverent in principle. Lot's wife really did turn to rubber, and that's *why* she turned to salt.

REFRAIN

Young folks, old folks, ev-'ry-bod-y come,
Join us at the Sun-day School and make your-self at home.
Please check your chew-ing gum and ra-zors at the door, And you'll

hear some Bi - ble sto - ries that you nev - er heard be - fore. 1. God

made the world in six days and rest - ed on the sev - enth; Ac -

cord - ing to the con - tract it should have been the e - lev - enth. But the

car - pen - ters were out on strike and the ma - sons would - n't work, so the

fore - man dug a hole and they filled it up with dirt. *(refrain)*

6 Noah was a weather man, and he predicted rain,
  Folks said they'd be darned if they'd be fooled
    that way again,
  So they went off on a picnic, and the rain
    began to fall,
  Old Noah had the laugh on them, he didn't get
    wet at all.   (refrain)

2 When they finished with the firmament they
    started on the sky,
  They hung it out overhead and left it there to dry,
  They studded it with stars made out of pretty
    damsel's eyes
  For to give us a little light when the moon
    forgot to rise.   (refrain)

3 Adam was the first man that ever was invented,
  He lived all alone, so he hardly was contented,
  They made him out of clay, and they thought
    he could get by,
  For that's the way they scraped along in all
    the days gone by.   (refrain)

7 Noah became a mariner and sailed around the
    sea
  With half a dozen wives and a whole menagerie,
  He tried his hand at fishing, so the Bible tale
    confirms,
  But he didn't have much luck because he only
    had two worms.   (refrain)

8 He failed the first season when it rained too
    heavily,
  For in that kind of weather no circus ever pays,
  For forty days and forty nights they sailed all
    around
  Till one wife kicked the lioness out because
    she was a blond.   (refrain)

4 Adam was a gardener and Eve became his
    spouse,
  They lost their job for stealing fruit and took
    to keeping house,
  They scrounged about and managed and were
    happy in the main
  Till they moved into the suburbs and started
    raising Cain.   (refrain)

5 Methusaleh was crabby 'cause he couldn't take
    a joke,
  He had all the makings of an old and seedy
    bloke,
  His whiskers got so long that he couldn't see
    ahead,
  If he'd tucked in all the corners he could've used
    them for his bed.   (refrain)

9 There are plenty of these Bible tales, I'll tell
    you more tomorrow,
  How Lot, with his wife and family fled from
    Sodom and Gomorrah,
  But his wife turned to rubber, so she settled
    on the spot,
  She was fixed up for a monument and missed
    a happy Lot.   (refrain)

111

10 Esau was a cowboy, a wild-and-woolly rake,
  Half the ranch belonged to him and half to
    his brother Jake,
  Now Esau thought the title to the property
    wasn't clear,
  So he sold out to his brother for a sandwich
    and a beer.   *(refrain)*

11 Samson was a husky guy from the P. T. Barnum
    school,
  He used to lift five hundred pounds as
    strongman in the show,
  Till a lady named Delilah got him all filled up
    with gin,
  They caught him bald-headed, and the coppers
    ran him in.   *(refrain)*

12 But Samson wasn't satisfied, the pace got in
    his hair,
  He mooned around when the act was on and
    set himself a chair,
  He'd slain ten thousand Philistines with the
    jawbone of a mouse,
  But that weight-lift of Samson's was what
    brought down the house.   *(refrain)*

13 David was a sheep-man, and a scrappy little cuss,
  They showed him Goliath just a-spoiling for a
    fuss,
  Now David didn't want to fight, but he was
    told he must,
  So he cotched up a cobblestone and bust
    Goliath's crust.   *(refrain)*

14 Elijah was a prophet who worked the county
    fairs,
  He advertised his act with a pair of dancing
    bears,
  He held a sale of prophecies 'most every
    afternoon
  And he went up every evening in a gaudy silk
    balloon.   *(refrain)*

15 Ahab had a lovely wife, her name was Jezebel,
  While hanging out the clothes one day, down
    off the roof she fell,
  "Your wife has gone all to the dogs," is what
    they told the king,
  And Ahab said he'd never heard of such a
    doggone thing.   *(refrain)*

16 Daniel was a naughty boy who wouldn't mind
    the king,
  The people said they'd never known of such a
    silly thing,
  They chucked him down a manhole, to a lion's
    den beneath,
  But Daniel was a dentist, and he pulled the
    lions' teeth.   *(refrain)*

17 Jonah was a traveling man, so runs the Bible tale,
  He booked steerage passage in a transatlantic
    whale,
  The cooking and conveniences, they weren't of
    the best,
  So Jonah pressed the button and the whale did
    the rest.   *(refrain)*

18 Salome was a chorus girl who had a winning way,
  She was the star attraction in King Herod's
    cabaret,
  Although you wouldn't guess that discretion was
    her rule,
  She's the favorite illustration figure in our
    Sunday School.   *(refrain)*

19 You can say she was a dancer, she did the
    hootchy kootch,
  The girls complained about her, 'cause she
    didn't wear very mooch,
  The king said, "My dear, you can't go around
    so bare,"
  But Salome said, "The heck I can't!" and kicked
    the chandelier.   *(refrain)*

NOTES

The abbreviated references in these notes are for comparison to original source materials from the Catskill Mountain area. The full titles for these references are listed in the Bibliography on page 125. The items marked thus (°) contain musical relatives. We hope these further references will be of interest to scholars and folklorists and also to the average singer and player who may wish to delve more deeply into the origins of these songs.

A-ROVING. Songs like this may be found in most collections of sailors' songs, which is why so many landlubbers buy them. The tune is carefully shaped to the words so as to produce suspense ("Mark well what I do say") even where the outcome seems tame. It is not very certain whether the girl was innocent, or was just playing innocent, but it may be that she just learned very quickly; that is, about money. The song doesn't tell what she wept about. Probably she was tired from so much walking with sand in her shoes, and she just needed to relax.

BIBLE STORIES. Many good people and experts, too, have devoted their efforts to bringing the full meaning of Biblical events closer to popular understanding by transforming older forms of wording and references that have become obscure into current expression. In this song we find numerous familiar passages treated in this highly reverent but down-to-earth fashion, so that remote tales seem quite up-to-date; that is, up-to-date of about sixty years ago. There is some difficulty in the lines about Lot's wife for, as we recall, the blotter report had her turn to salt, and not rubber, which was unknown at the time. The explanation is that the term "to rubber" is used as a verb, as in neck. Our guess is that after this Sunday School lesson most children forget to claim their chewing-gum and razors on the way out.

BILLY BOY. The qualities of Billy's "young thing" are seldom clear in the many versions we have heard, but apparently she knew just what to do in the clinches. Our text definitely does not derive from *Lord Randall* (Child Ballad No. 12), and the only important similarity with that song we can find is that Billy also fain would lie down. Most of our lines occur in *Beadle's Dime Song Book No. 10*, 1863, and the tune is from a Catskill square-dance version played on harmonica and guitar by Ernie Sager (see *Dances from Woodland*, second edition, 1955).

BLACK IS THE COLOR. This finely wrought and expressive love song occurs in English songsters of about 1800, though it is probably much older and of Scottish origin. Like a number of complaining songs, such as *Old Smoky* and *I Know My Love*, it has suffered from inversion; that is, a text crying out against the perfidy of a man towards the girl who loves him has been changed, somewhat deliberately, into a wail by a self-styled man over a girl's independence. Somebody must have been very much ashamed, whenever this inverted form was begun, and the weakened texts cannot support a melody strain as moving as this. The tune has appeared in collections from the South (Campbell, Henry) and has also been tampered with for chiefly non-musical ends. Our version comes from Massachusetts, and it seems to drift off towards the North.

BLOW THE MAN DOWN. A number of sailors' songs are made up of a series of comparisons between a pretty girl and a ship. The device must have encouraged many young men to go a-sailing. Much ingenuity has been devoted to those details of description that lend themselves best to double meanings. Most prominent is usually the roundness of the counter, but more subtle and, indeed, more the central point of the tale is the reference to the young clipper, a favorite of sailing ship days that has not grown obsolete in the slightest. The full description is so realistic that we have had some difficulty in convincing young college ladies that Radcliffe Highway was a legitimate place-name in the song. Our version of the tune is widely known, and resembles most a form recorded in Jamaica, West Indies.

BOLD GRENADIER, THE. This song was learned from George Edwards of Sundown, New York. It is best known under the title *The Nightingale's Song* or *One Morning in May*. A seventeenth-century broadside version in the Roxburghe Collection is called *The Nightingale's Song; or, The Soldier's rare Musick, and Maid's Recreation*. The delicacy of expression hidden in the stylized broadside language is not always appreciated here, and some kindly souls have taken quite literally the musical references to bird songs and violin playing, and found them appropriate to collections of school and camping songs. George Edwards did remark to us that he thought the situation rather neatly put, and declared that, as in many of his songs, "There's no harm in it, there's no harm to anyone." Versions of the song have been widely noted in the South and Middle West of the United States, sufficiently so as to suggest the influence of a smuggled printed distribution quite appropriate to Fundamentalist regions. Oral and printed versions seem strangely lacking in England, in Canada, and in the Northeast generally, and our tune seems unique among traditional melodies for this or other songs. We have sometimes wondered what would happen if some soldier played a 'cello instead of a fiddle.

JFSS VIII/194; *SFQ* II/154, VIII/171; *Belden* 239; *Cambiaire* 92; *Combs* 2 20; *Cox* 2 78; *Eddy* 230; *Henry* 200; *Lomax* 2 183; *Morris* 360; *Niles* 1 #11; *Randolph* I/266; *Roxburghe* IX/70; *Sandburg* 136; *Scarborough* 310, 438; *Sharp* 6 II/192; *Thomas* 1 112; *United States* 3 21; *Wyman* 1 68.

BRATS OF JEREMIAH, THE. No other version of *Unhappy Jeremiah* is known to us from oral tradition. Texts appeared in Eton's Song Book of the late 1840s and in Beadle's Dime Song Book No. 3, 1859, where we also find a parody "reply" called *Happy Hezekiah*. Cutting quotes the lines from a manuscript copy located in the Adirondack region of New York State. None of the texts indicate a tune or refrain. Some opening sentiments of the song, with an equivalent tune and stanza form, may be found in versions of *Devilish Mary.* The tune learned from Etson Van Wagner resembles George Edwards' song THE SHIP'S CARPENTER, and we find it used for several versions of *The Gypsy Laddie,* so that following scholarly tradition we would be obliged to head our song Child Ballad #200, if it were only more legitimate.

Beadle #3/44; *Campbell* 112°; *Creighton 2* 72°; *Cutting* 50; *Davis* 590°; *Flanders 1* 91°, 190°; *Randolph* III/188°; *Sharp 4* I/233°, II/200°, 225°.

CAPTAIN WALKER'S COURTSHIP. American texts of this riddle-image ballad, better known in standard form as *Captain Wedderburn's Courtship,* Child Ballad #46, are rare. This version was sung by George Edwards, and the tune, of course, is Irish, a variant of George Edwards' tune for FAIR JULIAN BOND, or the ballad of *William Reilly,* which has been used for a number of other songs as well. Barry has quite properly suggested Irish sources generally for the few complete versions of our song that have appeared in Maine, Nova Scotia, and Massachusetts, so that its roots in "the English and Scottish Popular Ballads" is at least open to question, Child having remarked upon an Irish form. But then many other "short form" riddle songs of several strains have been blithely and uncritically labeled "Child Ballad No. 46," as if these perfectly nice songs must give way to academic protocol. We need not belabor the point that the questions asked in CAPTAIN WALKER'S COURTSHIP are mostly to be found in Child Ballad #1, *Riddles Wisely Expounded,* and that "primary" derivations have been asserted on far slimmer connections, be they only from the South. In our version the right tone for the riddles is set in the by-play, where it appears that the girl from Maiden Lane knew enough to reserve her place, just in case Captain Walker thought he knew all the answers.

Ref. in *Coffin* 46, also: *JAFL* XXIV/340°, XXIX/157, LII/38°; *JFSS* III/110°, 114°; *Broadwood* 6; *Child* I #1, #46, V/216, 414; *Christie* II/48; *Creighton 1* 92°; *Creighton 2* 21, 162; *Eddy* 25; *Gardner 2* 139; *Greig* 33; *Henry* 140; *Jamieson* II/154; *O'Neill* #7°; *Ord* 416; *Petrie* #510°; *Scarborough* 230; *Sharp 4* II/190, 225°; *Shay 1* 126; *Vaughan-Williams* 82°.

DEVIL AND THE FARMER'S WIFE, THE. Very many versions are known of this merry tale, though of the several strains none show the particular tune and refrain form sung by Marvin Yale. The theme of the song is quite old, and it was already in print by 1630 as *How the Divell was guld by a scould.* An old Scottish form was rewritten by Robert Burns as *The Carle of Kellyburnbraes,* and it may well be argued also that the tale grew out of Irish lore. Under the title *The Farmer's Curst Wife* it has been enshrined in the Child Collection as #278. Oral versions in widely varying forms are known all over the United States

and Canada. Thus it is natural that many elements in a framework already suggestive of imaginative expansion have been shifted, varied, omitted, and improvised upon in delightful ways. The whimsical concept of the Devil as a "damn fool" in our version is otherwise reported only from Maine and Nova Scotia. Extensive variation has also been applied to the nonsense refrain forms. Strains that include a whistled portion are quite common, but the transcription of Marvin Yale's version in the collection by Downes and Siegmeister, which is faulty in several other respects, has a whistling refrain incorrectly inserted. Marvin Yale, as was his habit, sang the blithe ditty in a doleful and pensive manner, deliberately out of keeping with its substance. We have drawn upon many sources, not so much to fill in an already adequate story in connected sequence as to utilize the many ingenious developments which add the "merely corroborative detail" to "an otherwise bald and unconvincing narrative."

Ref. in *Coffin* 148, also: *JAFL* XXVII/68°; *JFSS* II/184, III/132; *JIFSS* XVIII/27; *Beck 2* 157; *Bell* 204; *Burns* 245; *Chase* 23; *Child* V #278; *Creighton 2* 95; *Fowke* 172; *Gordon 1* 12.20.23, 1.10.24; *Goss* 126°; *Jamieson* I/305; *Johnson* IV/392; *Mackay* II/91; *O Lochlainn* 108; *Rollins* #1162; *Roxburghe* V/367; *Williams* 211.

DEVILISH MARY. Many elements have combined to form this assertive song, including the well-known *I Know Where I'm Going,* the little-known *Sweet Little Willie,* and a few others. What holds these together is a tune that so fits the character of the blithe and brazen Mary or Katie that no further connections are needed, and we can readily fill in for ourselves a continuous narrative. When a girl knows her own mind as Mary does, the boys have reason to be wary: that is the burden of the song.

DOWN BY THE GREENWOOD SHADY. The Child Ballad title for this is *The Cruel Mother,* #20. Rollins lists the earliest English print from 1638, while Greig shows a Scottish tradition. Numerous versions are known from both sides of the Atlantic, and some comment has been made on the "herb magic" values of the nonsense refrain lines. The implications of the tale as represented in popular tradition go quite contrary to the interpretation shown by Child's title. It is not so much the cruelty of the mother that is evident as her own shame and suffering, which reflect more on the failures of social responsibility and on barbaric attitudes centered upon the hypocritical righteousness of the male and the automatic blame of the weak and tortured woman. The most striking feature of Marvin Yale's version is the formation of the tune, for which we have found only one distant parallel of outline (Creighton 1) of the large number of tunes observed. The way in which the third line of each stanza, with the same words as the first, has its tune repeated for the fourth line, which moves ahead with the story into unexpectedly strong detail, is more dramatic than anything that could have been planned. The repetition of the melodic pattern has the effect of lulling our judgment of the words, so that the enormity of the meaning dawns upon us rather suddenly in a kind of delayed reaction. This effect was carried out also in the style of singing, for Marvin Yale took plenty of time for exaggerated expression in the opening of the tune, but he "deedled" on quite casually through the third and fourth lines. The treatment is subtle and fascinating; akin to the same singer's slow and dolorous rendering of the bright ditty about MISSIE MOUSE.

Ref. in *Coffin* 50, also: *BFSSNE* VIII/7; *JFSS* II/109, III/70, VI/80; *Allingham* 279; *Buchan* II/207, 211; *Child* I #20, III/502, IV/451, V/413; *Christie* I/105, 107; *Creighton 1* 3°; *Creighton 2* 16; *Goss* 16; *Greig* 21; *Kinloch* 44; *Mackay* II/55; *Quiller-Couch* 102; *Rollins* 45; *Sharp 3* 35; *Williams* 295.

EARLY ONE MORNING. The fine melody and first stanza are well known and deservedly reprinted. But the substance of this song hardly ever appears, and in our opinion the omissions are hardly accidental. They fit in with a rather deplorable practice in some recent treatments of folksongs of evading passages spelling out the perfidy of men, or transfering the onus of false lover to the woman. We have remarked how BLACK IS THE COLOR and some other traditional songs have been spoiled in this fashion. The contrived implication of the male's superiority does not meet any objective evaluation, and it is also reprehensible for its attribution to popular sentiment of pretenses that belong almost entirely to self-consciously sophisticated groups. The full text of our song appeared at least as early as 1828 in The Songster's Magazine (Ritson).

FLAT RIVER RAFTSMAN, THE. After some speculative efforts, the full story of the origins of this song has been made plain (Gardner 2/267). Both Jack Haggerty and Ann Tucker have been identified as known individuals, and the tale of jilting has also been exposed as a fiction motivated by lumber camp intrigue. Flat River, Michigan, rises in Six Lakes, has a power-mill site at Greenville, and joins the Grand River below Lowell and above Grand Rapids. In most versions the brokenhearted raftsman departs for Muskegon. Some of the lines in the song have a somewhat literary and sophisticated cast which adds to the undercurrent of humor. The romantic phrases, which often meant little to the lumber camp singer, have been more or less altered or "mistaken" in sense, while resemblances of sound values have been preserved. This is a remarkably musical treatment of language, for the resulting "words" may have no meaning at all,

or they may be rationalized into an entirely strange sensibleness, and preserved for their rhythm and tone. Such changes are explained away in far shrewder manner by the folk singer than by the more naïve song hunter. For example, the description of Ann Tucker as having a "neck like a doughnut," in our text, is probably unique as a poetic usage. George Edwards "explained" that this phrase meant slender and graceful, claiming that the term "doughnut" properly means the long, slim, untwisted variety, whereas the common round dainty with the hole should be called "cruller." This is pretty convincing reasoning, until we find in several other versions of the song the corresponding line, "Her form was like the dove, so slender and neat." A similar difficulty occurs in a version given by Beck, one line reading "she has broken the rigon that Good would soon tie." The word "rigon," Beck explains, means something like "thingamajig" or "do-whacker." Far more likely it is merely a close sound-equivalent of "rigging." We need not be too trusting, or too lacking in humor, when such rationalizations are offered, even when the singer himself seems to believe them. One line (Gardner 2), "My virtue's departure, alas, I defame," shows an almost deliberate fol-de-rol covering the mock poetry of "All mirth is departed." It took some questioning to elicit from the singing of George Edwards the rather flowery phrase, "the small darts of Cupid." This appears in other versions as "the streamlets dark acoople" and "the cold ports of Cuba." These instances show much of what happens in the process of oral transmission of songs. The process is most striking and fitting, of course, when the text was initially composed with some pretence to literary style. We need hardly elaborate on the observation that the late nineteenth-century parlor style had little of the language usage of lumbermen or raftsmen, or indeed of anyone else. Sooner or later, as the song is repeated and handed on, the more lush phrases are brought into uneasy accord with more familiar experience and expression. And often, as in this case, the by-product is a subtle but unmistakable amusement on the part of the singer. The trained interpreter of "art" songs tends to take himself so seriously and his material so unsmilingly that his texts and melodies lose much of their original creative impulse. Perhaps the "note" musician has much to learn from the refreshing freedom and irreverence of manner of the lumber camp singer, who can turn even his forgetfulness and "mistakes" into a valid kind of emotional expression. George Edwards' tune for THE FLAT RIVER RAFTSMAN is of a strain widely used for this song, though other tunes have been noted. The tune has been used for some other songs, and Charles Hinckley gave a slight variant, which he named *The Flat River Girl,* for his original ballad *The Hills of Last Chance.*

JAFL XLVIII/344; *PTFLS* VII/176; *Barry 2* 74°;

Beck 1 123; *Beck 2* 140°, 149; *Carmer* 17; *Eckstorm* 124; *Gardner 2* 267°; *Gordon 2* 61; *Laws* 61; *Linscott* 214; *Lomax 2* 268; *Rickaby 3*, 10°; *Sandburg* 392; *Shay 2* 140°; *Shoemaker* 218.

HI, HO, JERUM. Here is another example of bringing heavenly affairs down to earth. The sprightly tune and Sunday-School moral are undoubtedly of Negro origin, and are appropriately akin to the parade-rhythm variety of spiritual. The highly mannered contrived rhymes show some relation to the technique found in *Peter Gray*. It is possible that the nonsense lines had something to do with the name of St. Jerome originally, but they are more likely just exuberant sounds on which to hang a melody.

I KNOW MY LOVE. This is another "complaining song" which has suffered recently from inversion; that is, the substitution of a deceiving girl for the false man. As penalty, the text of the changed forms are regularly defective, and the sparkling lilt of the tune is lost at the same time. The uneven beat seems a fitting accompaniment to the "troubled mind" that "knows no rest." While the short Irish form (Hughes) is most familiar, there is some indication that the tale began with an older Scottish song. The raucous and widespread *There's a Tavern in the Town* is a relatively recent commercial re-writing of this song.

ISLAND OF JAMAICA, THE. Flanders remarks that this rare song is a "favorite practical joke whimsy" among seamen and woodsmen. The convivial ending is a delightful note, deliberately out of keeping with the expectations aroused in the listeners of the development of the romance. In its theme the song is related to the numerous forms of *The Little Mohee*, and impinges somewhat on the story of *The Girl I Left Behind*. The hero is named variously Henry Orrison, Henry Woolson, or Henry Rysall. Versions have been noted only in Maine, Vermont, New Brunswick, and Nova Scotia, so that the song is remarkably localized in its spread, while no printed source is known. George Edwards' unusual tune is of Irish cast, and is not known elsewhere for this or other traditional songs. The variety of ballad clichés that fall victim to satire is matched only by an imaginative treatment that extends to the singer's laughter at his own rôle in lumber camp life. Not many writers of the "educated" styles, particularly of the nineteenth-century era when the ballad surely originated, could have abandoned their cultivated self-importance in so sophisticated a fashion.

Creighton 1 73; *Flanders 2* 27.

I WISH I WAS A SINGLE GIRL. Judging from the better-known song that follows, marriage can be a burden instead of a joy for the man, let him be unfortunate in his choice. And never fear that all and sundry will not hear endlessly of his complaints. Yet these are relatively small matters (however large they may loom for the individual man) and result from avoidable mistakes. Not so for the misfortunes of the woman subjected to marriage, whose plaints are the more severe because, unlike the man, she has had less choice, and cannot as easily get out from under. The trials of a poor marriage have been unequally distributed, and in this eloquent song we are made to feel the full weight of daily drudgery and unending regret. The song is most likely of Negro origin.

I WISH I WERE SINGLE AGAIN. We may not sympathize with the man who was careless enough to make the same mistake twice, especially as he has usually told about it in barber-shop style. This less common version of a familiar tale of woe comes from Massachusetts. It has an endless type of melody and some apparently unrelated episodes. But we are very much taken with Nancy O, for the refrain is a "sleeper," and the dawn will come suddenly after a few repetitions, all on a summer's morning.

I WAS THERE ALMOST. The tradition of treating Biblical themes and times in current language and reference is combined with the tall tale in this song. The stretching of the truth, in Mark Twain's phrase, is done very flagrantly and boldly, and deliberate garbling of well-known matters as well as a careless juxtaposition of serious moments and slapstick produce a well-defined character for the singer's rôle. We have collated numerous versions from oral sources, since nearly everyone remembers a stanza or two, and if it comes out wrong, what difference does it really make to you?

I WONDER WHEN I SHALL BE MARRIED. The old maid of any age who has lost hope has remained a pathetic figure in every age, more pitiable when career-girl opportunities were lacking which might have provided not only some real independence but also the requisite social contacts. Of the many songs, humorous and sympathetic at the same time, which treat of the familiar figure, this early nineteenth-century example is particularly poignant, because the character that emerges is not only in a bad way, but has been given a bad start. Obviously in every spelled-out detail the maid has been shielded from human relations and activities and left to coddle with minor articles of adornment, which have for her become substitutes and symbols. Her unhappy conviction that life and love can be based on her store of trinkets bespeaks the unreal world from which she can no longer emerge, yet it is hard indeed to face the truth that she has nothing to offer. The song has been traditional in Scotland, and was adapted by Robert

Burns, though the older text has appeared in such prints as The Universal Songster of 1836.

JACKIE ROVER. This song is not very long because Jackie wastes neither time nor opportunity. His ups and downs are not all on horseback, since he also rides on something or other called a "diddle-i-day," believed to be a corruption of holiday, though he was going to some kind of market. We have adapted the lines from a Massachusetts version, but according to another from West Virginia, Jackie ties up the maid's garter, a detail we find too suggestive. The tune strain resembles our version for THE BOLD SOLDIER.

JENNIFER GENTLY. Our title derives from the non-sense refrain, which provides another example of the "herb burthen" tradition. This song is one of the several traditional strains dealing with the taming of the gentle wife, regarding which we must recall that the term "gentle" does not refer at all to her personal qualities of tenderness but rather to her origin in a family of higher station, hence unprepared for a normal sharing of daily tasks. Other strains involving the sheepskin method of progressive education are best known as *The Wee Cooper O' Fife* and *Dando*. The moral might be drawn differently, of course, as proposing the advisability of a couple talking things over a bit before marriage, if they can contain themselves long enough for prosaic matters. The *Dando* form of the song has been heard in the Catskill area, and Etson Van Wagner tried to palm it off as a song from the Dutch tradition, knowing we were interested in such, on the strength of the nonsense refrain "tinna clinnama clinchama clingo." Since the tune is formed around two polar tetrachords, and is both pentatonic and hex-atonic in outline, we leave it to the experts of Cecil Sharp House to determine the mode.

JOLLY BOATSWAIN, THE. George Edwards' song is of a far better-known strain than Etson Van Wagner's treatment of the same traditional theme in THE TROOPER AND THE TAILOR. Still another variant of the tale is known as *The Charleston Merchant,* and the discovery of the lover motif appears also in WILLIE THE WEAVER and in *The Dog in the Closet*. In the Roxburghe Collection we find an early broadside, attributed to one Martin Parker, called *The Cooper of Norfolke*: or A pretty Jest of a Brewer and the Cooper's Wife: And how the Cooper served the Brewer in his kind. That text in turn may be traceable to a still earlier form of the story. Much effort has been devoted to demonstrating the thematic source in a twelfth-century French *fabliau*, in Boccaccio's *Decameron* and in the laundry-basket episode in Shake-speare's *Merry Wives of Windsor*. But the search for early literary record of a theme, when there are no connections of anything unique and concrete that would demonstrate historical ties, testifies merely to the patience of the investigator and to the assumed virtues of anything that has appeared in print, the latter concept directly opposed to the nature of song in popular tradition. The diversion of thought serves in fact to bolster the upside-down doctrine of Louise Pound and others, that music and poetry seep down into the lowly forms of popular currency out of the overflow from the inspired and self-sustaining crea-tivity of an élite, which nobody bothers to remind us has been quite consistently illiterate during the period considered important. It rarely occurs to our more speculative theoirsts that such a view merely reflects a present-day if outmoded bias known as the "trickle-down" theory of economic prosperity. Sober second thought necessarily leads to the observation of a large accumulation of popular poetic motifs, as of musical motifs, drawn from the world of experience and con-tinually cast and re-cast into concrete forms. The high literary developments of value and appeal have grown precisely out of the existing store of popular motifs, and are constantly arising anew from them. It is not only incorrect, but also an underestimation of the nature of Boccaccio's and Shakespeare's art, to omit remark on their popular roots. They invented neither adultery nor the many entrancing situations to which it often leads; rather did they listen with respect to the tales of old. Versions of THE JOLLY BOATSWAIN are widely known in England, Canada, and the United States. Many of them employ the same tune strain as in the George Edwards form, which is also related to the singer's and others' tunes for THE OLD SPOTTED COW and some other traditional songs. A few versions, generally from areas near the Catskills, contain the specific end image of the trading off of the little tailor for China tea.

JAFL LII/64°; *JFSS* II/156°, III/253, VIII/131°; *SFQ* VIII/173; *Campbell* 163°; *L. Chappell* 93; *Christie* II/4°; *Cobb* 54; *Cox* 2 75; *Eddy* 143; *Flanders* 2 123; *Gilbert* 36; *Grainger* #180°; *Green-leaf* 112; *Henry* 191; *Morris* 371; *Roxburghe* I/99; *Sharp* I/338°.

KATE AND HER HORNS. A broadside text called *Crafty Kate of Colchester* dates from about 1690, and many prints of more recent time have appeared in this country. It is remarkable, given the early time of English provenance, that no versions of this de-lightful and carefully worded song have been noted in oral tradition except on this side of the Atlantic. The sense of the tale is that any wise Kate who would not be a fool can surely handle a mere man, given a grain of ingenuity and a pinch of humor. The tune used by George Edwards for this song is not found for any other version we have seen, but several English and Scottish forms of *Lord Bateman* use a similar tune strain. Unusual for songs of the Catskill tradition is the number of versions found in nearby localities of New York State, including texts noted by Thompson and by Cutting and a prose form from the Schoharie Hills (Gardner 1).

> *JFSS* I/240°; *Belden* 231; *Bobbing Around Songster* 212; *Combs 1* 157; *Creighton 2* 184; *Cutting* 74; *Flanders 2* 123; *W. Ford* #3199; *Forget-Me-Not Songster* 145; *Gardner 1* 387; *Grainger* #170° to 174°; *Greig* 43°; *Mackenzie* 325; *Roxburghe* VIII/430; *Sharp 4* I/405; *Shearin* 30; *Thompson* 413.

KATEY MOREY. Kittredge (*JAFL* XXXV/387) ascribes this song to an American broadside of about 1830, but collectors still follow the academic practice of labeling the ballad a "modern version of *The Baffled Knight*," Child #112. There is in fact no connection or parallel other than in the general theme, for which no copyrights can be issued. The most ingenuous of folklorists might well consider that outwitting a "sly and crafty rogue" is hardly unprecedented for a nimble maid, and that merry and instructive tales about how she manages this will quite naturally be long retained and elaborated in the memory of a people, emerging in concrete forms on any manner of occasions. Oral versions of this song have been noted from a number of American sources. Some of the texts have apparently been diluted and spoiled by a narrow prudery, in which the collectors show somewhat less ability in dealing with the way of a maid with a man than does our Katey. Even were we to fall in with such tender caution in our text, there would be no way of eliminating the cleverly wrought suggestive qualities of the "nonsense" refrain, without which the song would cease to exist. So we put aside mechanical derivations and any dilution of the plain meaning of the song, and upon adding the evidence from the musical side we may suggest that, broadside or "Child Ballad" patents or no, the kernel of *Katey Morey* belongs to Irish tradition. The tune strain shows this directly, and we find close relatives of the tune sung by George and "Dick" Edwards in the versions given by Gardner and by Lomax, the latter as sung by Aunt Molly Jackson. One other tune (Sharp) resembles the spiritual *Poor Wayfaring Stranger*, and this is a hardly remarkable if extreme transfer. The song has apparently long been a lumber camp favorite from Michigan to Ontario.

> Ref. in *Gardner 2* 393°, also see: *JAFL* XXXV/385, *Lomax 3* 122°, *Thompson* 411.

LAVENDER'S BLUE. This ditty dates from around 1680, and the opening survives today as a nursery song. Let the deep analysts tell us why. The mysterious dog who is so well liked in the story is the one that follows us everywhere. The moral seems to be that the lady ought always to be kind to the man's dog. The nonsense refrain lines belong to an activity song for a somewhat older age group. It is rather pleasant to read, regarding a Massachusetts version, that the song "is connected with the amusements of

Twelfth Night and refers to the choosing of the King and Queen of the festivities. It is significant to the place it holds in showing the diversions (!) and customs of the early days (!). In New England it has lost its place as a singing game (!)." May we suggest that some diversions, customs, games, or activities proper to a king and queen, while unobserved, may be readily imagined?

LEATHER-WINGED BAT, THE. This is a *condensed* record of a bird convention that took place before 1656. Various portions are sung here and there to this day, and all the implied advice from experience may be welcome to a young man in love and also to a young lady with a bird in hand. The tune for this song has been widely adapted for many others.

LET'S HAVE ANOTHER ROUND. The rare and localized lumber camp song here has had some portions noted by an anonymous hand in several prized volumes at Yale University's Library. The rollicking jig tune shows Irish traits. A version from Pennsylvania uses a mining town setting.

LITTLE CABIN BOY, THE. The title of this rare song is sometimes given for versions of *The 'Golden Vanity*,' with which it has no connection. The tragic tale tells with disarming frankness not only of the passion of a "lady so gay," but also of the extreme power held by a master over an apprentice. The outcome is all the more chilling because nothing more than a whim proved an insuperable obstacle to true love. Only one earlier record of this song is known to us (Christie Collection), and this is dated 1876. A tune for *Polly on the Shore*, noted in 1922, is related to George Edwards' tune here, but the fragmentary text shows no connection. This scarcity of reference is rather surpising, since the substance and the manner of THE LITTLE CABIN BOY is of a fairly common type. This is not the only instance in which we find it impossible to guess just how George Edwards came by the words and music of his songs, and perhaps it would be less difficult if there were no precedents at all.

> *JFSS* VII/7°; *Christie* I/242.

LITTLE SCOTCH GIRL, THE. This tale is said to relate to Colliestown, near Aberdeen. The ballad form was in print in 1828, and is known among scholars as *The Keach i' the Creel*, Child #281. Except for fragments found in Maine (Barry), the version we learned from George Edwards is the only one discovered in the United States. It has lost most of its Scottish dialect. The word "blue" means a woolen blanket, which can be used to cover up in several ways. The song neglects to tell us whether the girl's father ever got to sleep. The theme and much of its presentation are surely much older than the nineteenth century, when the present form attained publication, and the tale clearly belongs with the best traditions of Boccaccio and Chaucer, or rather with the popular motifs on which these masters drew. George Edwards' tune for this ballad does not occur elsewhere in traditional music, so far as we have been able to discover.

Barry 1 336; *Bell* 75; *Buchan* I/270; *Child* V #281, V/323, 348, 424; *Coffin* 150; *R. Ford* 277; *Greig* 230; *MacColl* 19.

LITTLE SPARROW, THE. Here is another courting and complaining song based on a bird image. It is related to but not derived from *The Cuckoo, The Turtle-Dove,* and *The Leather-Winged Bat.* Most versions have a tune strain like this, which may also be found in use for other songs and also for hymns.

LOLLY TOO-DUM. This well-known song is a fine example of the way in which nonsense refrain lines are so knit musically with the stanzas as to provide many meanings not directly given in the text, without changing of the refrains themselves. Perhaps an investigation of this feature of traditional songs would alter some expressed or implied feelings about the alleged poverty, deterioration, and formlessness of these songs, which somehow seems to the students to occur increasingly as the songs depart from a supposed aristocratic English standard from an assumed but undescribed Golden Age. The conventional opening on a private conversation "overheard" by the singer does not necessarily indicate an origin in the penny-sheet press. Our tune is a variant of the familiar strain.

MAID ON THE MOUNTAIN'S BROW, THE. This conversation song seems to have followed the rounds of the lumber camps in this country and in Canada. O Lochlainn gives an Irish version, and refers to a broadside. Most curious is the way in which the moral and the outcome of the song seem to vary among the few versions known, largely through the inclusion or the omission of stanzas. Dean's version places the man beyond criticism, and borrows lines from other songs to end on a clear assertion of the superior prerogatives of the male. O Lochlainn's text and the version of Mackenzie emphasize the flirtatious approach of the girl, which is unsuccessful. The other known texts make much of the pouting, still without favorable issue. Only in George Edwards' version is a solution reached in reconciliation and marriage. The girl does not seem more than usually coy, and her attitudes and knowing sense appear the more favorably as the man is made to feel properly ashamed. There is a refreshing frankness in the lines containing reproach, common to all versions, and it takes a humorless lapse indeed to swallow the thin shielding of its

direct reference. Thus one collector takes the distinct line "You rap and call, and pay for all, and go home at the break of day" to refer to payment for something called " 'hol," described as a local abbreviation for "alcohol." The home and the title of the maid vary from Logan Bough to Sweet Brown Knowe (knoll?) among the known texts. Only one other tune has been noted for this song, and it is unrelated to the daring and striding tune of George Edwards, which appears to have no relatives among traditional songs and which clearly violates nearly every precept about the simplicity of folk-song tunes. The sources generally show a lumber camp origin.

JAFL XLVIII/351; *Dean* 83; *Gardner 2* 122; *Greenleaf* 153°; *Mackenzie* 124; *O Lochlainn* 38.

MAID ON THE SHORE, THE. Though few versions of this song have been collected, it is apparently well known throughout the northeastern United States and nearby regions, once more showing lumber camp influence in its spread. Barry believes there ought to be a broadside source, not as yet located, but the text he gives from Maine is not as similar in wording as we might expect to other known forms, which would be likely if they came from a single printed original. Gordon believes his California text to be a hybrid of folk and broadside influences. Other versions come from Missouri, Pennsylvania, Newfoundland, and Nova Scotia, while a single stanza appears with the tune strain as #327 in the Joyce Collection from Ireland. Flanders recognizes this song as generally familiar in New England. None of the versions noted thus far are "so neat and complete" as the two Catskill forms. The influence of the mermaid, mist-maiden, or siren theme from Irish lore on this song is unmistakable, but the meaning of that influence can readily be exaggerated. Mackenzie draws elements of the song out of the ballad *Lady Isabel and the Elf Knight*, Child #4, and with Greenleaf and Mansfield he also suggests similarities to *Broomfield Hill*, Child #43. We may forego these speculations directed towards the prestige attaching to the Child Ballads in academic circles. Barry writes at length about the siren song motif, but instead of stopping with its clear indication in Irish legendry, he develops a more mystical and enshrouded derivation from ancient "bird-soul" myths traceable to both Scandinavia and to southern Europe. Joyce's title for the tune is *The Mermaid*, but the single stanza he gives is unmistakably the next to the last of this song. What does not seem to be remarked upon by the scholars is the motif that is most obvious to singers and hearers alike, which centers on the unexpected climax of the song, and requires of the maid no supernatural qualities for its full poetic justification. This motif is simply the turning of the tables on the eager, "superior" men who entice the "defenseless" maid towards an outcome everyone expects. After a carefully detailed build-up, she turns out to be more than a match for the self-assured captain and his "merrili crew," and she knows how to take advantage of their wine as well as of her own wiles, catching them off guard and earning applause from a safe distance, grudgingly from the men and delightedly from the rest of us. Today the views about the general helplessness of womankind ought to be set down as an outmoded, self-serving fiction among men, and it ought to require no more than her normal and known abilities for a maid to hold her own, even in adverse circumstances. It is no compliment to the maid to require that she be a literal siren in order to save herself. A number of nice tunes are associated with THE MAID ON THE SHORE, mostly related to the Irish strain of Joyce, and not attached to any other traditional song. Only a Newfoundland and a Nova Scotia version of the tunes have any relationship with the two noted in the Catskills, which are themselves of a single family, and even this relationship rests largely on the cadence pattern induced by the formation of the stanzas. Etson Van Wagner's tune has a haunting quality and polish that is quite remarkable, and we hasten to present it especially for the edification of the kindly souls who deal so mechanically with the classification of melodic modes in folk song on the inapplicable basis of the garbled modes of ancient Greek music as misinterpreted in the quite irrelevant medieval church mode theories. The similarities of words and music in the two Catskill versions we have heard give rise to a suspicion that George Edwards may have *learned* the song directly from his neighbor, while we were sitting by, during the several occasions when they both sang to us. At any rate, the opportunity was there, the time of singing several years later, and judging from his capacious repertory George Edwards surely needed little more hearing than this to make a song his own.

BFSSNE VII/12; *Barry* 2 40; *Belden* 107; *Fowke* 158; *Gordon 1* 8.15.27; *Greenleaf* 63; *Joyce* 152; *Karpeles* I/30; *Korson* 54; *Mackenzie* 74.

MICHAEL FINNIGIN. The misadventures of the unfortunate Michael are generally known in briefer form. What seldom appears is that not only the stanzas but the tune also is properly of circular construction. The name of the hero obviously derives from its susceptibility to rhymes, rather than the other way about.

MY DUCKSIE HAS FLED. This sailor-song theme from Massachusetts is related in part to George Edwards' unique song THE POOR COUNTRYMAN, and in part to the numerous complaining songs A-ROVING, BLOW THE MAN DOWN, *The Fireship*, and others. Related texts are known from Newfoundland and Nova Scotia. While the story of victimization is not as detailed here as in THE POOR COUNTRY-MAN, it is as plain as it is painful, and it supports a rewarding melody. A *ducksie* means a potential *slasher*.

MY PRETTY LITTLE MAID. Numerous conversation-piece songs deal with the conventional figures of the simple country maid and the sophisticated gallant who just happens to be passing by and just happens also to find a reason for dallying talk. *The Pretty Maid Milking Her Cow*, and in this volume ROLLING IN THE DEW and SEVENTEEN COME SUNDAY, as well as in some measure THE HILLS OF GLEN-SHEE, are examples of variations on this theme. Almost invariably the maid's quick-witted parries make the gallant seem properly foolish. If there is a moral here, it is that success with a maid cannot be attained by substituting talk where the situation calls for action. The maidenly devices in these songs are pretty and modest to hide their cleverness, and in this example they are wedded to a very fitting tune and a neat refrain.

OLD MAID'S LAMENT, THE. There is every evidence that this is a song of a young and pretty coquette, and not at all an old maid's complaint. There is too much direct appeal to be "taken away," and too obvious an expectation of numerous offers, combined with appreciation for the satire, to allow us to view the text as anything more than a theatrical sham. There are not many situations in which the brassy young thing can make quite so bold in public, while seemingly begging for sympathy. Most of our interpretation of this venerable song arises from the musical qualities of the tune and the refrain patterns, which suggest a lively dance with patter-song lyrics, swinging of the prop cocktail or cigarette tray, and an audacious demand to be contradicted. A broadside text from the Roxburghe Collection has evidently remained popular over some time, and it was reprinted in this country in The Columbian Harmonist of 1814. Today we may still get excited, but certainly not worried, about a young lady who can sing so cheerfully about how she has safely reached the age of twenty-six and is still available.

POOR COUNTRYMAN, THE. As with MY DUCKSIE HAS FLED, this song theme and certain specific images of the town and street names, the cab or cabin, the drinking scene and the leaving of the victim without clothes, all recur in two related songs, *Barrack Street* from Nova Scotia and *The Shirt and the Apron* from Newfoundland. There is no sailor protagonist, however; rather we find the butt of the humor in an inexperienced visitor or tourist. Certain of the situations are inimitably funny when combined with the tune, as the assessment of a bribe by the policeman and the squirrel-cage dance. We know of no direct relative of this song of George Edwards, and while the tune is of a familiar jig type, it has not turned up elsewhere in traditional sources. The self-conscious mention of a present occasion at the Fair for singing of the song recalls a similar humorous bit in THE NEWBURGH JAIL. The setting involving steamboat excursions would suggest a late nineteenth-century time for the story.

Creighton 1 226; *Greenleaf* 222.

ROLLING IN THE DEW. This is another of the conversation pieces relating to the simple country maid and the sophisticated gallant. Here the maid's replies are not only witty but suggestive of more than casual acquaintance with sporting by-play. And in this version, her frank admission of a healthy interest in early morning exercise may perhaps be even more disconcerting to the luckless young fool than the more usual pose of modesty. Certainly we can have no quarrel with the good sense of the nonsense refrain, as its full warmth becomes increasingly precise from the first stanza to the last.

ROVING PEDLAR, THE. Probably this is the original form of a song well known also in the two parody strains of *The Roving Irishman* and *The Roving Gambler*. The framework has proven sufficiently flexible to permit the retention of much of the detail and incident, with minor changes of place names and occupations serving to relate these to more familiar heroes. A broadside text appears in a songster of 1851, and the song is represented in lumber camp sources. No tune has appeared previously for this strain of songs, and the whimsical melody here of George Edwards seems to have no close relatives.

SFQ VIII/176; *Belden* 374; *Bobbing Around Songster* 210; *Dean* 124; *Laws* 222; *Lomax 1* 151; *Morris* 443; *Rickaby* 81; *Shearin* 13.

SEVENTEEN COME SUNDAY. This gay song is quite familiar in British sources, but only scattered note of it has appeared in oral tradition in this country. While English broadside texts are known, there is good reason to believe that these have stemmed from an older oral tradition common both in England and in Scotland. Such is generally the case with broadsides that have won any considerable and continuing popularity. One early re-working of the traditional theme appears in the poem of Robert Burns called *A Waukrife Minnie*. The conversation sequences present also fairly direct parallels with the songs MY PRETTY LITTLE MAID, ROLLING IN THE DEW, and *The Pretty Maid Milking Her Cow*, but the import as well as the outcome of the question and answer forms are quite different. There is no conventionalized derision of the maid's lowly station, and no battle of wits. But the blithe sauciness of the maid is chastened by methods widely known to be effective, and she shows a marked maturity in the end. A few versions in this country (Anderson, Cox, Lomax) show increasingly distant derivations, especially in their endings, from what is clearly the same strain. Several of the tunes in English sources, and one from Nova Scotia, resemble the tune sung by George and "Dick" Edwards, and we cannot tell where the numerous similar forms given by Grainger originated, but it is likely that the basic strain is Irish. We find it in the Petrie Collection with the title *Where Are You Going, My Pretty Maid*, but lacking a refrain.

JFSS I/92, II/9, 269, 274, IV/291, VI/7; *Anderson* 121; *Baring-Gould 2* 150°; *Burns* 228; *Cox 1* 394; *Cox 2* 83; *Creighton 2* 164°; *Eddy* 188; *Farnsworth* 8°; *R. Ford* 102°; *Grainger* #125° to #133°; *Johnson* IV/210; *Kidson* 2; *Lomax 1* 290; *Merrick* 16; *Petrie* #774°; *Sharp 1* I/4°; *Sharp 2* 68°; *Sharp 3* 138°; *Sharp 4* II/156.

SIMPLE LITTLE NANCY BROWN. We have been unable to trace any relatives of this little teasing song of Frank Joy. It lends itself readily to improvisation of additional stanzas, and the prolonged suspense of the nonsense refrain is not only intriguing but seems to cover up all sorts of interesting possibilities before the answer is given. The tune is obviously a variant of *London Bridge Is Falling Down*, yet it is clearly not a nursery song.

TROOPER AND THE TAILOR, THE. Etson Van Wagner sang this for us when his wife had stepped into the next room. The essential story is the same as in THE JOLLY BOATSWAIN and such relatives as *The Charleston Merchant*, yet the song is another and a different treatment of the theme, not a derivation or outgrowth. Neither the lines nor the images show connections, and these lines and images have a polish and delicacy of expression that can only result from a long and independent history. The form is nevertheless so rare that we know of only one previous version in which the wording and the situations have definite parallels. Even in this version the tune and the formation of the stanzas and refrain are not similar, and we do not find Etson Van Wagner's tune elsewhere in traditional song. The treatment of the familiar theme in this strain is remarkable for an exceedingly careful choice of words, somehow, also a personal characteristic of the singer. The "payment for lodging" is a neat excuse, the reference to "fun" is both adequately descriptive and simple, and the image of the "compliments and kisses" plus the offer of a warm bed make for gentle satire. Logically the trooper should have found these generous wiles irresistible. However, had he gone to bed, we would never hear the wonderful excuses for not burning up the cupboard, which did burn up the trooper.

JFSS VIII/274; *Roxburghe* I/99.

UNFORTUNATE MISS BAILEY. The text for this ironical song is attributed (Fowke) to George Colman, an English dramatist who died in 1794, though the tune is stated to have been in use for at least three earlier English songs. In its present form the tale must have been exceedingly popular over a long period, for we find the words reprinted in The Columbian Harmonist or Songster's Repository of 1815 and in Crockett's Free and Easy Song Book, edition of 1846, among others. Parodies, if we identify the tune and pattern with the *Miss Bailey* form, continued to be written, and the most famous of these was Andrew Jackson's campaign song *The Hunters of Kentucky*. The tune we have found seems the most singable variant. Perhaps the popularity of the song related especially to a period when people could still tell *ratafia* from prussic acid.

WAGONER'S LAD, THE. One of the many derivatives of *The Cuckoo* family of songs, elements of this complaint are quite often transferred from and to other strains where there is no relevance to the image of the horses not eating the hay. Versions of A-WALKIN' AND A-TALKIN' *Old Smoky, Rye Whiskey,* and a number of other songs often contain this and other portions of the story in jumbled fashion, yet in our form there is a distinct and connected theme wedded to a variant of one of the many tunes associated with the mixed strains. It is characteristic of the fully developed traditional song that sympathy is aroused for the situation and motivation of each character, so that we recognize the proper feeling of the girl at the same time that we agree with the man's necessary assertion of his independence.

WEST VIRGINIA BOYS, THE. The warnings against entanglements have been referred to boys from just about any neighboring state whose agricultural resources may deserve ridicule. Somehow poor soil and poor manners are made to go together, and the irrational attractiveness of the mountain lad characters is completely overlooked, while the description of the presumably refined young ladies leaves us with some doubt about how much status they are able to lose. There is nothing to show that the disparaging descriptions have interfered anywhere with the normal impulses of courtship, nor with the general rise in population along state borders. Naturally our tune did not come from the Catskill area.

WHAT CAN THE MATTER BE? It has seemed to us that the fuller text, and not merely the opening stanza, is required so that the feeling associated with the widely appreciated melody may be crystallized. The measure of the girl's excitable impatience, her concern with the trivial but precious marks of affection and tributes to her charms, produce an atmosphere that well supports the wound-up forward movement of the melody. Besides, it gives us some motivation for Johnny's delay, if we assume he is at all reticent under unfair pressure. Early texts of the song appeared in Johnson's Musical Museum and in The Royal Songster or The British Chaunter of about 1800 (Ritson Collection).

WIFE WHO WAS DUMB, THE. The blithe old ditty about the man who couldn't leave well enough alone dates from a broadside of about 1678. *The Dumb Wife* appeared in the numerous editions of Pills to Purge Melancholy from 1698 to 1719. A story on the same theme by Anatole France is said to derive from a passage in Rabelais, which itself suggests still earlier origins. Traditional versions of our song are scarce in the United States, and all probably stem from broadside prints, at least one (W. C. Ford) from before 1800; others are De Marsan (1860) and Wehman (1892). In all likelihood more people know the song than would care to announce it, at least when their wives are present. George Edwards' tune here is, for once, traceable to related sources. De Marsan's print specifies as air the Irish tune *Cowskeen Lawn*. In the version given by Moffat, that air is closely similar to THE WIFE WHO WAS DUMB, and has the same developed stanza formation. Moffat further traces *The Cruiskeen Lawn* to an Irish derivative of an old Scottish tune for *John Anderson, My Jo,* the traditional song later adapted by Burns, as it is found in the Skene Manuscript, written about 1615 to 1620. We may observe thus that some considerable age is established for both the text and the melody of our song, though it has not therefore been elevated to membership in the approved list of Child Ballads. New York State seems somehow to have best retained a familiarity with this merry ditty. Besides our very complete form, one version (Gardner 1) comes from Conesville, in the nearby Schohaire Hills, while another in the Ring Manuscript was taken down at Clinton Corners. But no other tune recovered from oral tradition belongs to George Edwards' *Cruiskeen Lawn* strain.
    JAFL LVII/282; SFQ V/181; *An Antidote Against Melancholy* (1884) 77; *Baring-Gould 1* II/54; *W. Chappell* I/120; *Cobb* 57; *De Marsan 1* #87; *Eddy* 214; *R. Ford* 32; *W. Ford* #2989; *Gardner 1* 199; *Joyce* 196°; *Korson* 56; *Moffat 1* 136°; *Moffat 2* 102; *Morris* 379; *Randolph* III/119; *Ring* 64; *Roxburghe* IV/355; *Wehman* #33/10.

WILLIE THE WEAVER. Here is still another merry tale of illicit sport, akin to THE JOLLY BOATSWAIN and THE TROOPER AND THE TAILOR and some others. The intervention of the gossiping neighbor and the advance suspicions of the husband are, however, distinct elements which also appear in a Vermont song called *The Dog in the Closet*, which has however an entirely different outcome. Peculiar to this song is the surprise ending of self-assertion by the wife, after Willie has been put out of the situation for good. The smoking chimney images may be related to the old haunting-song *My Good Old Man,* but in this case we may better call it a kind of hunting-song. Variants of our circular tune occur in some other versions of the song.

WON'T YOU SIT WITH ME AWHILE? We find this text an adaptation from a polite songster of 1842, and it has in fact an exceedingly moral lesson. The fellow in the story thinks of all the hedges down by the riverside. He picks on a young one just because she is reluctant. The girl thinks he says he will marry her, but all he says is that he won't marry anyone else. Then he blames the girl for giving in. Not nice, except the full-blooded melody, but it all goes to show how much you have to watch out for that extra inch above the knee.

BIBLIOGRAPHY

Allingham, William. *The Ballad Book.* London: Macmillan, 1864.

Anderson, Geneva. *A collection of ballads and songs from East Tennessee.* Thesis (ms.), University of North Carolina, 1932.

1 Baring-Gould, Sabine. *English Minstrelsie.* 8 vols., Edinburgh: Grange Publishing Works, 1895.

2 Baring-Gould, Sabine; Sheppard, H. Fleetwood; Bussell, F.W. *Songs of the West.* London: Methnen & Co., 1913.

1 Barry, Phillips; Eckstorm, Fannie Hardy; Smith, Mary Winslow. *British Ballads from Maine.* New Haven: Yale University Press, 1929.

2 Barry, Phillips. *The Maine Woods Songster.* Cambridge: Powell Printing Co., 1939.

Beadle's Dime Song Books, #1, 1859–.

1 Beck, Earl Clifton. *Songs of the Michigan Lumberjacks.* Ann Arbor: University of Michigan Press, 1941.

2 Beck, Earl Clifton. *Lore of the Lumber Camps.* Ann Arbor: University of Michigan Press, 1948.

Belden, Henry M. *Ballads and songs collected by the Missouri Folk-Lore Society. University of Missouri Studies,* XV No. 1, 1940.

Bell, Robert. *Ancient Poems.* London: John W. Parker & Sons, 1857.

Bobbing Around Songster, The. Philadelphia and New York: Fisher and Brother, 1851.

Broadwood, Lucy E.; Fuller-Maitland, J.A. *English County Songs.* London: The Leadenhall Press, 1893.

Buchan, Peter. *Ancient Ballads and Songs of the North of Scotland.* 2 vols., Edinburgh: William Patterson, 1875 (first edition, 1828).

BFSSNE *Bulletin of the Folk Song Society of the North East,* 1930-1938.

Burns, Robert. *Complete Poetical Works.* Cambridge Edition, Houghton Mifflin, 1897.

Cambiaire, Célestin Pierre. *East Tennessee and Western Virginia Mountain Ballads.* London: The Mitre Press, 1934.

Campbell, Olive Dame; Sharp, Cecil J. *English Folk Songs from the Southern Appalachians.* New York: G. Putnam's Sons, 1917.

Carmer, Carl; Sirmay, Albert. *Songs of the Rivers of America.* New York: Farrar & Rinehart, 1942.

Cazden, Norman. *Dances from Woodland.* Bridgeport (Connecticut), 1955 (first edition, 1945).

L. Chappell, Louis W. *Folk-Songs of Roanoke and the Albemarle.* Morgantown (West Virginia): The Ballad Press, 1939.

W. Chappell, William. *Popular Music of Olden Time.* 2 vols., London, 1859.

Chase, Richard. *Old Songs and Singing Games.* Chapel Hill: University of North Carolina Press, 1938.

Child, Francis James. *The English and Scottish Popular Ballads.* 5 vols., Boston and New York: Houghton Mifflin, 1882-1894.

Christie, William. *Traditional Ballad Airs.* 2 vols., Edinburgh: 1876, 1881.

Cobb, Lucy Maria. *Traditional ballads and songs of eastern North Carolina.* Thesis (ms.), University of North Carolina, 1927.

Coffin, Tristram P. *The British Traditional Ballad in North America.* Philadelphia: The American Folklore Society, Bibliographical Series Vol. II, 1950.

1 Combs, Josiah H. *Folk-Songs du Midi des États-Unis.* Paris: Les Presses Universitaires de France, 1925.

2 Combs, Josiah H.; Mixson, Keith. *Folk Songs from the Kentucky Highlands.* New York: G. Schirmer, 1939.

1 Cox, John Harrington. *Folk-Songs of the South.* Cambridge: Harvard University Press, 1925.

2 Cox, John Harrington. *Traditional Ballads, Mainly from West Virginia.* United States, Works Progress Administration, Federal Theatre Project, National Service Bureau, Folk-Song and Folklore Department Publication #75-s, 1939.

1 Creighton, Helen. *Songs and Ballads from Nova Scotia.* Toronto: J. M. Dent, 1932.

2 Creighton, Helen; Senior, Dorren H. *Traditional Songs from Nova Scotia.* Toronto: The Ryerson Press, 1950.

Cutting, Edith B. *Lore of an Adirondack County.* Ithaca: Cornell University Press, 1944.

Davis, Arthur Kyle. *Traditional Ballads of Virginia.* Cambridge: Harvard University Press, 1929.

Dean, Michael C. *The Flying Cloud.* Virginia (Minnesota), 1922.

De Marsan, Henry, and others. *American Songs and*

Ballads, a collection of 467 broadsides issued in New York and Philadelphia ca. 1860. (New York Public Library, *MP–U.S.).

Eckstorm, Fannie Hardy; Smith, Mary Winslow. *Minstrelsy of Maine.* Boston: Houghton Mifflin, 1927.

Eddy, Mary O. *Ballads and Songs from Ohio.* New York: J. J. Augustin, 1939.

Farnsworth, Charles H.; Sharp, Cecil J. *Folk-Songs, Chanteys and Singing Games.* London: Novello, n.d.

1 Flanders, Helen Hartness; Brown, George. *Vermont Folk-Songs and Ballads.* Brattleboro: Stephen Daye Press, 1931.

2 Flanders, Helen Hartness; Ballard, Elizabeth Flanders; Brown, George; Barry, Phillips. *The New Green Mountain Songster.* New Haven: Yale University Press, 1939.

R. Ford, Robert. *Vagabond Songs and Ballads of Scotland.* Paisley: Alexander Gardner, 1904 (first edition, 1899).

W. Ford, Worthington Chauncey. *Broadsides, Ballads & c. Printed in Massachusetts, 1639-1800. Massachusetts Historical Society, Collections,* Vol. 75, 1922.

Forget-Me-Not Songster, The. New York: Nafis and Cornish, 1842.

Fowke, Edith Fulton; Johnston, Richard. *Folk Songs of Canada.* Waterloo (Ontario): Waterloo Music Co. Ltd., 1954.

1 Gardner, Emelyn Elizabeth. *Folklore from the Schoharie Hills.* Ann Arbor: University of Michigan Press, 1937.

2 Gardner, Emelyn Elizabeth; Chickering, Geraldine Jencks. *Ballads and Songs of Southern Michigan.* Ann Arbor: University of Michigan Press, 1939.

Gilbert, Douglas. *Lost Chords.* New York: Doubleday Doran, 1942.

1 Gordon, Robert Winslow. *Old Songs That Men Have Sung. Adventure Magazine,* July 10, 1923 to October 15, 1927. (Collected volume in Music Division, Library of Congress).

2 Gordon, Robert Winslow. *Folk-Songs of America.* United States, Works Progress Administration, Federal Theatre Project, National Service Bureau, Folksong and Folklore Department, Publications, 1938.

Goss, John. *Ballads of Britain.* London: John Lane, 1937.

Grainger, Percy; Grainger, Rose. *Collection of English Folksongs, Sea Chanties, etc., #19, 26, 44, 100-300.* (Hektographed, 1907). (New York Public Library, Music Division).

Greenleaf, Elisabeth Bristol; Mansfield, Grace Yarrow. *Ballads and Sea Songs of Newfoundland.* Cambridge: Harvard University Press, 1933.

Greig, Gavin. *Last Leaves of Traditional Ballads and Ballad Airs.* Aberdeen: The Buchan Club, 1925.

Henry, Mellinger Edward. *Folk-Songs from the Southern Highlands.* New York: J. J. Augustin, 1938.

Jamieson, Robert. *Popular Ballads and Songs.* 2 vols., Edinburgh: Archibald Constable & Co., 1806-1808.

Johnson, James. *The Scots Musical Museum,* edited by Robert Burns. 6 vols., Edinburgh, 1839 (first edition, 1787-1803).

JAFL *Journal of American Folklore,* 1888–.

JFSS *Journal of the Folk Song Society* (London), 1890-1931.

JIFSS *Journal of the Irish Folk Song Society,* 1904–.

Joyce, Patrick Weston. *Old Irish Folk Music and Songs.* Dublin: Hodges, Figgis & Co. Ltd., 1909.

Karpeles, Maud. *Folk Songs from Newfoundland.* 2 vols., London: Oxford University Press, 1934.

Kidson, Frank. *A Garland of English Folk-Songs.* London: Ascherberg, Hopwood and Crew, n.d.

Kinloch, George Ritchie. *The Ballad Book.* Edinburgh, 1891 (reprint).

Korson, George. *Pennsylvania Songs and Legends.* Philadelphia: University of Pennsylvania Press, 1949.

Laws, G. Malcolm, Jr. *Native American Balladry.* Philadelphia: The American Folklore Society, *Bibliographical Series* Vol. I, 1950.

Linscott, Eloise Hubbard. *Folk Songs of Old New England.* New York: Macmillan, 1939.

1 Lomax, John A.; Lomax, Alan. *American Ballads and Folk Songs.* New York: Macmillan, 1934.

2 Lomax, John A.; Lomax, Alan. *Cowboy Songs.* New York: Macmillan, 1938 (first edition, 1910).

3 Lomax, John A.; Lomax, Alan; Seeger, Ruth Crawford. *Our Singing Country.* New York: Macmillan, 1941.

MacColl, Ewen. *Personal Choice of Scottish Folksongs and Ballads.* New York: Hargail Music Press, 1956.

Mackay, Charles; Pittman, J.; Brown, Colin. *The Songs of Scotland.* 2 vols., London: Boosey & Co., 1877.

Mackenzie, William Roy. *Ballads and Sea Songs from Nova Scotia.* Cambridge: Harvard University Press, 1928.

Merrick, W. Percy; Vaughan-Williams, Ralph; Robins, Albert. *Folk Songs from Sussex.* London: Novello, 1912.

1 Moffat, Alfred. *Minstrelsy of Ireland.* London: Augener & Co., 1897.

2 Moffat, Alfred. *The Minstrelsy of England.* London: Bayley and Ferguson, 1901.

Morris, Alton Chester. *Folksongs of Florida.* Gainesville: University of Florida Press, 1950.

Niles, John Jacob. *Songs of the Hill-Folk.* New York: G. Schirmer, 1934.

O Lochlainn, Colin. *Irish Street Ballads.* London: Constable & Co., 1939.

O'Neill, Captain Francis. *Waifs and Strays of Gaelic Melody.* Chicago: Lyon & Healy, 1922.

Ord, John. *The Bothy Songs and Ballads.* Paisley: Alexander Gardner, 1930.

Petrie, George. *The Complete Collection of Irish Music.* London: Boosey & Co., 1902-1905.

PTFLS *Publications of the Texas Folk Lore Society,* 1926–.

Quiller-Couch, Arthur. *The Oxford Book of Ballads.* Oxford: Clarendon Press, 1932 (first edition, 1910).

Randolph, Vance. *Ozark Folksongs.* 4 vols., Columbia (Missouri): The State Historical Society of Missouri, 1946-1950.

Rickaby, Franz Lee. *Ballads and Songs of the Shanty-Boy*. Cambridge: Harvard University Press, 1926.

Ring, Constance Varney; Beckwith, Martha. *Mid-Hudson Popular Songs and Verse*. Ms. Microfilm in Vassar College Library, Poughkeepsie, 1937.

Ritson, Joseph. *A collection of thirty-seven popular songbooks, c. 1800*. (Yale University Library I b 57 t 800).

Rollins, Hyder E. *An analytical index to the ballad entries (1557-1709) in the register of the company of stationers of London*. Chapel Hill: University of North Carolina Press, 1924.

Roxburghe Ballads, The. Edited by William Chappell and J. W. Ebsworth. 8 vols., London: The Ballad Society, 1868-1895.

Sandburg, Carl. *The American Songbag*. New York: Harcourt Brace, 1927.

Scarborough, Dorothy. *A Song Catcher in the Southern Mountains*. N. Y.:Columbia University Press, 1937.

1 Sharp, Cecil J. *Folk Songs from Somerset*. 3 vols., London: Novello, 1908-1910.

2 Sharp, Cecil J. *English Folk-Song: Some Conclusions*. London: Simpkin & Co., 1907.

3 Sharp, Cecil J. *One Hundred English Folk-Songs*. Boston: Oliver Ditson, 1916.

4 Sharp, Cecil J.; Campbell, Olive Dame; Karpeles, Maud. *English Folk-Songs from the Southern Appalachians*. 2 vols., London: Oxford University Press, 1932.

1 Shay, Frank. *More Pious Friends and Drunken Companions*. New York: Macaulay, 1928.

2 Shay, Frank. *Drawn from the Wood*. New York: Macaulay, 1929.

Shearin, Hubert G.; Combs, Josiah H. *A Syllabus of Kentucky Folk-Songs*. Lexington: ` Transylvania Printing Co., 1911.

Shoemaker, Henry Wharton. *Mountain Minstrelsy of Pennsylvania*. Philadelphia: Newman F. McGirr, 1931.

SFQ *Southern Folklore Quarterly*, 1937—.

Thomas, Jean. *Devil's Ditties*. Chicago: W. Wilbur Hatfield, 1931.

Thompson, Harold W. *Body, Boots and Britches*. Philadelphia (New York): J. P. Lippincott, 1940.

United States, Works Projects Administration, Federal Music Project, Kentucky. *Folk Songs from East Kentucky*. 2 vols., 1939.

Universal Songster, The, or Museum of Mirth. 3 vols., London: Jones & Co., 1832-1837.

Vaughan-Williams, Ralph; Sharp, Cecil J. *Folk Songs from the Eastern Counties*. London: Novello, 1908.

Wehman, Henry J. *Wehman's Collection of Songs*, 1886—.

Williams, Alfred. *Folk Songs of the Upper Thames*. London: Novello, n.d.

Wyman, Loraine; Brockway, Howard. *Lonesome Tunes*. New York: H. W. Gray Co., 1916.